Between March 1987 and July 1988, 391 people lost their lives in three British disasters: the sinking of the _Herald of Free Enterprise_ at Zeebrugge, the King's Cross Fire, and the explosion on the Piper Alpha oil platform. None of these was an Act of God: none of them should have happened. Each of them was preceded by detailed warnings and dangers.

Judith Cook examines these three disasters in detail. She traces a common pattern: warnings of problems and dangers ignored in the interests of cutting costs and maximising profits – and then disaster.

She then looks at other areas to find what warnings are being sounded, and how much notice is being taken of them – what are the risks of a mid-air collision, another ferry disaster, an explosion at one of our nuclear power stations? What dangers are built in to the existing designs for the Channel Tunnel? And what about the slow-fuse disasters, the accumulation of toxic and nuclear waste in the UK, the build-up of dangerous residues in our food and water, the green-house effect and the hole in the sky?

In every area, Judith Cook finds that warnings are being sounded and dangers are being ignored. She makes proposals for tougher controls, better safeguards and more effective responses – but, above all, she demands an attitude of mind, starting at the top, that puts the lives of people before the pursuit of profit.

An Accident
Waiting to Happen

An Accident
Waiting to Happen

JUDITH COOK

UNWIN
PAPERBACKS

LONDON SYDNEY WELLINGTON

First published in paperback by Unwin Paperbacks, an imprint of
Unwin Hyman Limited, in 1989.

Unwin Hyman Limited
15–17 Broadwick Street
London W1V 1FP

Allen & Unwin Australia Pty Ltd
8 Napier Street, North Sydney, NSW 2060, Australia

Allen & Unwin New Zealand Pty Ltd with the Port Nicholson Press
Compusales Building, 75 Ghuznee Street, Wellington, New Zealand

British Library Cataloguing in Publication Data
Cook, Judith, *1933–*
    An accident waiting to happen.
1. Man-made disasters, ca 1930–1979. Case studies
I. Title
909.8′2
ISBN 0-04-440434-3

Typeset in 10½ on 12 point Baskerville by Cambridge Photosetting Services
and printed in Great Britain by Cox & Wyman, Reading

Contents

Acknowledgements

Many people have helped me with material for this book. In fact, I have never had so much assistance with any other project. This shows the strength of the concern now felt in so many diverse quarters about the growing threat of disasters which might well have been prevented.

My thanks are due therefore to Frank Dobson, MP, for all his help with documentation and information on the King's Cross fire; Mr A. J. F. Foot for sharing his concern over the demise of the Trinity House pilots; Bill Brett of the Institution of Professional Civil Servants for help with regard to Air Traffic Control and Pilot Fatigue; Andrew Lees of Friends of the Earth and his office for assistance on pollution; David Matthews of the Fire Brigades Union for help on King's Cross and the Channel Tunnel; Roger Lyons and Roger Spill of the Manufacturing, Science and Finance Union for information on Piper Alpha and problems in the North Sea oil industry; Mr Julian Parker of the Nautical Institute for assistance on the safety of Ro-Ro ferries; Dr Robin Russell-Jones for information on the ozone layer and other aspects of pollution; and finally, Will Thorn and Tom Keene of Television South West for the Lowermoor Water Treatment Plant story.

Help was also gratefully received from the Birmingham Trades Union Research Unit; the Royal Institution of Naval Architects; Greenpeace; the National Union of Seamen; the Fire Brigades Union; and the Press Association Library.

On a personal level my thanks to Jim Reynolds who promoted the idea and has been a tower of strength, and to Michael Pountney who, rare in the world of publishing today, kept in touch and gave encouragement all along the line.

Prologue

I owe it to my younger son, Nicholas, that I was not myself, a statistic in a disaster.

At the end of February 1974, as a freelance journalist, I had a commission to interview various people working in the theatre in Paris, including British director Peter Brook.

Nicholas had a thing about air crashes (we had had quite a time persuading him to go on a family holiday to Majorca the previous year), and he begged me not to fly. I made non-committal replies but time was short and, although it was more expensive, I decided I would fly and say nothing.

Just before I was due to return home I discovered that there was an industrial dispute which had grounded all flights by the then British European Airways, so I went along to the nearest ticket office to inquire what I should do, as my flight was for the following Sunday, 3 March. The only possibility, I was told, was a seat on a DC10 belonging to Turkish Airlines. I duly booked.

When I rang home that Friday night I spoke to both my sons and my youngest daughter. 'You won't fly home, will you?', begged my son. 'Promise?' I did.

On the Saturday morning I mulled over what I should do. We were, at that time, a single-parent family. Nicholas would never know that I had flown and it would save so much time. I would also lose the money paid out for the flight and we were not at all well off. Lastly, a nice evening had been planned for me by friends including a special meal out in a Paris restaurant. But then I had promised. Just supposing . . .

Eventually, consumed by guilt, I rang and cancelled my booking and, somewhat ruefully, changed all my plans for the Saturday evening in order to make the long journey back to England by train and ferry. The friends with whom I was staying tried to persuade me to stay. It was very tempting.

I resisted temptation however and, on Saturday afternoon caught the boat-train from the Gare du Nord, finally arriving back in Ipswich, where we were living, late that evening.

Around lunchtime the next day news came of the crash of that Turkish Airlines DC10 with 346 people on board. Not one of them survived.

It is that easy to become just a statistic in a disaster.

1 Disasters

There have always been, and always will be, accidents, catastrophes and disasters but they divide into two broad categories – those which could not have been foreseen and, therefore, could not have been avoided; and those where the writing was on the wall for a long time. Into the first broad category go the natural disasters, the eruptions of volcanoes, the hurricanes and floods – although the latter, along with famine, can all too often now be laid at the door of man.

It is those in the second category that are examined in this book, those which were waiting to happen.

Had I been one of the 346 victims of the DC10 on 3 March 1974, then my death would have fitted neatly into the pattern. One baggage handler left the cargo door open and this was at the root of what was to come. But he was only the end of a chain. Behind him, as the authors of the book, *Destination Disaster*, say, lay a history of failure by the management of McDonnell Douglas who built the aircraft to respond 'to repeated warnings and two actual demonstrations of the hazard; the chilling predictions of the catastrophe that actually occurred'.

They quote a memo written on 27 June 1972 by F. D. Applegate, director of Product Engineering, Convair Division of General Dynamics Corporation (subcontractors to the McDonnell Douglas Corporation). He says:

> The potential for long-term Convair liability on the DC10 has been causing me increasing concern for several reasons ... The airplane demonstrated an inherent susceptibility to catastrophic failure when exposed to explosive decompression of the cargo compartment in 1970 tests ...
>
> It seems to me inevitable that, in the twenty years ahead of us, DC10 cargo doors will come open and cargo compartments will experience decompression for other reasons and I would expect this to usually result in the loss of the airplane. It is recommended

that overtures be made at the highest management level to persuade Douglas to immediately make a decision to incorporate changes in the DC10 door which will correct the fundamental cabin floor catastrophic failure mode ...

Nothing, of course, was done. There were other factors too. For reasons still unexplained the records of that particular aircraft had been falsified. It had also had a hasty and premature promotion to the jumbo-jet league of Turkish Airlines and insufficient attention had been given to the safety of its passengers by the Federal Aviation Authority.

What followed was also classic – horror, enormous coverage by the media, a prolonged legal wrangle over compensation lasting years and a whole range of excuses for what went wrong. It is all pretty academic to those who never reached the end of that flight. You are, as they say, a long time dead.

Preventable disasters are much in the news at the moment because we have had three in this country between March 1987 and July 1988 – the sinking of the *Herald of Free Enterprise*, the King's Cross fire and the explosion of the Piper Alpha oil platform. In all, 391 people died within the space of sixteen months.

Before examining these in some detail – along with others which may possibly be in the pipeline – it is worth looking briefly at some other recent accidents.

At about 3.40 on the afternoon of 11 May 1985 a fire started in block G of the main stand of the Bradford City football ground at Valley Parade. Within five minutes the whole stand was in total flames and 56 people lost their lives. The subsequent inquiry found that the fire was started by a lighted match or cigarette falling on to a pile of rubbish under the stand, rubbish which had built up steadily over the years, having fallen through gaps and holes in the floor. The rapid spread of the fire was due to the stand being made of wood with an asphalt roof.

There was no firefighting equipment inside the stand. As the fire spread, people in the stand tried desperately to get out the easiest way, through the doors at the back of the stand where they had come in, only to find that many of the doors were locked while others opened inwards, causing great problems owing to the crush of people trying to get out. The turnstiles could not be used as exits as they only let people in.

Later it was discovered that the club had been told all about the safety problems posed by the ageing stand by both the police and the Health and Safety Executive. Action was due to be taken two days after the fire broke out. A letter from the West Yorkshire Metropolitan County Council in July 1984 had expressed concern to the secretary of the club about the build-up of rubbish under that stand. 'The carelessly discarded cigarette could give rise to a fire risk', it said. It also pointed out that people should be able to get out of the stand quickly.

Three months later, on 22 August, a Boeing 737 belonging to British Airtours burst into flames on the runway at Ringway airport near Manchester. At the time of writing – over three years later – the results of the inquiry into that accident have still not been published. From what is known it seems that there was an explosion in the engine which caused a piece of debris to smash a hole in the left-hand wing's fuel tank. Fire broke out on that wing and towards the back of the plane, as it was about to take off. The pilot brought the plane to a standstill and ordered it to be evacuated but that was easier said than done. Some exits could not be opened at all because of the fire, others stuck initially causing evacuation to be slow.

The cause of death of the 55 people was due to the 'inhalation of fumes' according to the pathologist's report at the subsequent inquest. Identification, said the coroner, had in many cases only been possible through dental records. It is not possible to pre-empt the findings of the inquiry, of course, but in the aftermath of the accident a great deal was said about the need to make cabin fittings and seats out of material less likely to give off toxic fumes (and there had been many general warnings about the hazards of fumes from existing materials), and to ensure exits were easy to use. At the time plans were afoot to remove two exits from aircraft on some routes in order to squeeze in more passengers. It has also been said that the use of smoke hoods would have meant that passengers might not have been so affected by the toxic fumes. Unfortunately, we are still waiting to see if this accident, even if it could not have been avoided, might at least have had less serious consequences.

It would be possible to go back further than 1985 – to other air crashes, to the 'Summerland' fire on the Isle of Man which killed 50 people, to Aberfan where there had been warnings for years of water under the tip and its instability.

Way back in 1977 three academics from the Open University, Victor Bignell, Geoffrey Peters and Christopher Pym, published a study, *Catastrophic Failures*, which looked at seven disasters and warned that the lessons from previous catastrophes were not being learned quickly enough, as inquiries and commissions took so long to report that fresh and avoidable disasters continued to take place. On some occasions the findings are overtaken by events and are obsolete before publication. They suggested that when there is such a disaster an interim report should be published just as soon as the main points have emerged so that action could be taken quickly. It does not appear that this advice has been heeded.

Very rarely, as we shall see, does it emerge that just one single thing went wrong. It is usually a combination of circumstances – equipment failure, management failure, human error, all too often compounded by lack of judgement and failure to heed advice or warnings.

All the classic ingredients were present in the cases of the *Herald of Free Enterprise*, King's Cross and Piper Alpha. At the very least we should seek to learn something from them.

The same kind of warning signals are already flickering in other areas – such as the possibility of a mid-air collision in our over-congested skies, a marine collision in the Channel, an accident to one of the ageing reactors at a nuclear power station, a fire in the Channel Tunnel when it is operating if safeguards are not built in . . .

If there is all too often a pattern to the buildup to a disaster there is certainly one afterwards. It happens. Great courage is shown by the rescue services in trying to help survivors, sometimes to the point of their own deaths. There is enormous media coverage, some of it of the new thrusting type which is totally tasteless. 'What did it feel like to see your husband/wife/child drown in front of your eyes?' 'What did you think when the plane burst into flames?' 'Are you happy your husband/mother survived?' What are people expected to answer?

For a short while the bemused victims or their relatives are bathed in a glare of publicity. There is great public sympathy and usually a disaster fund is set up to which people give generously. All too often this, also, can become a miserable bone of contention. The government announces it will set up an inquiry. Court battles for compensation begin.

The disaster soon passes out of the news and eventually is only of interest to those closely involved who, bewildered, no longer find themselves of any interest to anyone else and possibly have to settle down to a lonely fight. The world has moved on.

Yet, as Donne says, 'any man's death diminishes me, because I am involv'd in Mankind'.

The coroner at the inquest into the victims of the accident at Ringway airport commented: 'During the ensuing months I think we should all remember that what I will be dealing with is an investigation into the deaths of fifty-five individuals and not just a number of persons linked together in a tragic accident'.

2 Zeebrugge

I still don't sleep properly. It all still runs through my mind and even when I do sleep I'm dreaming about it . . . I dreamed of my friend on there the other night. She kept saying to me: 'I'm not dead, Gail. I'm still with you'.

Gail Cook, survivor

Legal Expenses Cover
We are advised by Brokers the following insurance cover can be available based on 1700 Ratings . . . defending criminal prosecutions, Health and Safety, leaving bow doors open, etc. The cost of this is approximately £3.40 per head per annum . . .

3rd clause of suggested insurance cover in P & O internal memo to officers,
8 July 1987 – sixteen months after the Zeebrugge disaster

A photograph on the cover of a booklet issued by the relatives of those who died on the *Herald of Free Enterprise*, the Herald Families Association, shows a roll-on, roll-off ferry (what is popularly known as a Ro-Ro ferry) capsized and on its side. Under it is a newspaper headline which says, 'How did it happen?'

Inside the booklet, the opening paragraph reads:

This is NOT the *Herald of Free Enterprise* – the picture and headline on the previous page appeared in December 1982, four and a half years before the Zeebrugge Ferry Disaster. It is the *European Gateway*, owned by Townsend Thoresen (now P & O Ferries). The *European Gateway* capsized after a collision in shallow water off Harwich in 1982 with the loss of six lives. It sank in less than four minutes.

On March 6 this year another Townsend Thoresen ferry, the *Herald of Free Enterprise* capsized and sank off Zeebrugge with the loss of 193 lives. It sank in less than five minutes. The Herald Families Association, formed by the bereaved of many of the 193 victims of the Zeebrugge Disaster, believes that this picture and headline express the essence of our concern. The headline asked, four and a half years before the *Herald of Free Enterprise* capsized and sank in minutes: 'How could it happen?'

The *European Gateway* was not the only Ro-Ro ferry to roll over and sink within minutes although it was the first in British waters. The others were *Jolly Azzurro* in 1978, *Collo* in 1980, *Sloman Ranger*, also in 1980, *Enis* in 1981 and the *Mont Louis* in 1984. All these capsized and sank as a result of collision.

The weather on 6 March 1987 was good. There was a light easterly breeze and very little sea or swell and the 459 or so passengers of the *Herald of Free Enterprise* (the exact count has never been known), could look forward to a calm and uneventful trip across the Channel to Dover. Many of them were day trippers and included a group who had taken advantage of an offer in the *Sun* newspaper. The ship, under the command of Captain David Lewry, had a crew of 80. Down in the car decks there were 81 cars, 47 freight vehicles and three others. Only after the tragedy did it transpire that the ship was also carrying drums of toxic waste.

Shortly after 6 o'clock in the evening the ferry left Zeebrugge and, in the formal words of the report of the subsequent inquiry:

The *Herald* passed the outer mole at 18.24. She capsized four minutes later. During the final moments she turned rapidly to starboard and was prevented from sinking totally by reason only that her port side took the ground in shallow water. The *Herald* came to rest on a heading of 136° with her starboard side above the surface. Water rapidly filled the ship below the surface level with the result that not less than 150 passengers and 38 members of the crew lost their lives. Many others were injured. The position in which the *Herald* came to rest was less than seven cables from the harbour entrance . . .

The statements of survivors are more graphic.

The guy who was in the news because he held his baby out of the water with his teeth was in the vicinity when I was down there. I saw the baby being taken on a rope out of one of the smashed windows. As the baby went up, the tears started coming to my eyes. It was tremendous to see someone so young coming out alive. But halfway up, the rope must have been yanked too hard and the baby bumped into the side of the ship. That was dreadful and stayed in my mind for days. It wasn't until the middle of the next week when I saw the same man on the TV news that I knew the baby was OK. He'd lost his wife, but the baby was only bruised. (Steve Homewood, assistant purser).

Jock Calderwood, a lorry driver, told waiting reporters: 'We turned over because the boat took in too much water. We shouldn't have sailed. The hold started flooding. I've sailed on this ferry about 50 times before and they have been having trouble with the doors for ages.'

A few more statements will suffice: 'I started to get lifejackets out of the way, stacking them up on the seats. But even then the people still alive couldn't get to the ladder because there were about five dead bodies at the base . . . while I was guiding the bodies up, the diver was trying to keep the heads of those who were alive above the water, as a few were going under now with the cold'. 'We were finding anything to break the windows – lifeboat axes, boathooks, anything we could lay our hands on.' 'It was really difficult. Sometimes people would slip out of the rope and hit me. I was hanging there at times supporting people on my back.' 'I found out later how one of the stewardesses, a friend of mine, Jenny Leslie, nearly died. She was in the perfume shop when it happened. There was a little boy sitting on the counter. She felt the ship shudder a little and then it started going. She grabbed hold of the child and pushed him to the back of the shop. She went to a lifejacket locker, gave the boy one and started handing them out until there were none left. So she took hers off and gave it away. The person she gave it to then pushed her out of the way, trod on her and she fell into the water.'

On 9 March John Moore, then Secretary of State for Transport, made a statement in the House of Commons:

Shortly before 7 p.m. GMT on Friday 6 March, the roll-on/roll-off passenger ferry *Herald of Free Enterprise* capsized, without warning, in a position about three-quarters of a mile outside the entrance of the port of Zeebrugge. She had left about half an hour before on a passage to Dover. It is my sad duty to inform the House that a total of 53 people are known to have died and 82 others are believed to be missing. A total of 408 passengers and crew were rescued.

As can be seen, the number of deaths was greatly underestimated.

On the same day John Moore, using the powers vested in him by Section 55 of the Merchant Shipping Act of 1970, ordered a formal investigation to be held; and it has to be said straight away that the inquiry was not only one of the fastest and most thorough but one of the most efficiently organized and constituted of any inquiry there has ever been into such a tragedy. It also published its report speedily. It was opened on 27 April 1987, only seven weeks after the disaster happened. It was also noted at the time the inquiry was set up, that Townsend Car Ferries (formerly Townsend Thoresen Ferries) was now, and had been at the time of the accident, a subsidiary of the Peninsular and Oriental Navigation Company (P & O), which had taken over Townsend Thoresen shortly before.

There was no shortage of immediate speculation as to the cause of the disaster and newspaper reports speak of shoals, of the ferry hitting a sandbank or some unspecified object which made a hole near her bows. It soon became apparent, however, that the answer was a much simpler one. The ferry had been allowed to sail with its huge bow doors *open*.

The media, especially the tabloids, were quick to find scapegoats. First and foremost was young Mark Victor Stanley, the assistant bosun whose job it was to ensure the bow doors had been shut. He, it transpired, was in his cabin asleep. The ship's master, Captain David Lewry, also came in for a pounding, including highly libellous statements that he had a drink problem. These had to be smartly withdrawn after it was revealed that he had undergone tests for drink and drugs after the ship sank. It was soon to appear that there were others who bore at least as large, if not a larger, share of responsibility for what happened and they were not on the ferry at all.

The judge appointed to the investigation into the sinking was Mr Justice Sheen, who proved an exemplary choice.

The inquiry began with a description of the type of ferry involved. She was a triple screw Ro-Ro passenger ferry built by

Schichau Unterweser in Bremerhaven in 1980, so she was a reasonably new ship. One extremely important point about the design of this type of ferry is that the car decks – for obvious reasons because the whole function of the ship is to allow vehicles to roll on and roll off – were not separated into sections by watertight bulkheads. What happens when a ship begins to sink without such bulkheads throughout the vessel was amply demonstrated in 1912 by the 'unsinkable' *Titanic*.

Doubts about construction and safety had been expressed before March 1987. The independent organization, British Marine Technology (BMT) (formed in 1985 from the National Marine Institute and the British Shipping Research Association), had looked at the safety record of Ro-Ro ferries in northern European waters between 1978 and 1983 and found some 2,113 incidents, of which 1,352 were identified as 'serious'. According to the Birmingham Trades Union Resource Centre, which has undertaken a good deal of research for the Dover branch of the National Union of Seamen, BMT then carried out tests on models in November 1986 and, unhappy with the results, suggested a two-year programme of safety research which would have cost the ferry companies about £10,000 each. The only taker was the little Sally Line.

After the disaster they tried again, suggesting this time a three-year study costing in all some £900,000 – £15,000 from each ferry company, the rest to be met by the government with the remit that it should look at critical factors leading to flooding and capsizing, suggest short-term measures and develop risk analysis against which ferry designs could be declared satisfactory or otherwise. At the time of writing (Autumn 1988), there are still no takers.

The *Herald of Free Enterprise* was designed for the Dover–Calais run where there are two ramps at different levels which unload the two decks. The port of Zeebrugge has only one ramp and one level and so that vehicles could reach the ramp from the upper deck, water was pumped into the forward ballast tanks to lower the bow. The ferry therefore usually set sail with much of the water still inside and being pumped out. On 6 March, with the bow doors also left open, as the ship turned to port at a speed of about fifteen knots, the combination was too much, the water swilled in and capsized her. The evacuation procedures allowed thirty minutes to get everyone off the ship. In the event the ship capsized in one and sank in four.

If Mr Justice Sheen was exemplary, then praise must also be given to Mr David Steel, QC, representing the Secretary of State for Transport, John Moore. He spared nothing and no one. On the question of design he invited the judge and his expert assessors to consider whether any design changes in passenger car ferries were needed. He said the vast undivided area of the car deck, the low freeboard and the high superstructure all made roll-on/roll-off ferries exceptionally susceptible to human error. But surprisingly there seemed to be no specific requirement in present maritime law for the bow door to be closed, and no stringent penalties for failing to do so.

As the report was later to state:

The *Herald* capsized because she went to sea with her inner and outer bow doors open. From the outset, Mr Mark Victor Stanley, who was the assistant bosun, has accepted that it was his duty to close the bow doors at the time of departure from Zeebrugge and that he failed to carry out this duty. Mr Stanley had opened the bow doors on arrival in Zeebrugge. Thereafter he was engaged in supervising members of the crew in maintenance and cleaning the ship until he was released from work by the bosun, Mr Ayling. Mr Stanley then went to his cabin where he fell asleep and was not awakened by the call 'Harbour Stations', which was given over the Tannoy address system. He remained on his bunk until he was thrown out of it when the *Herald* began to capsize. Mr Stanley has frankly recognised his failure to turn up for duty and he will, no doubt, suffer remorse for a long time to come.

At the inquiry Mr David Steel, QC, said:

I hope that people will not too readily jump to the conclusion that Mr Stanley failed in his duties. You will have to consider the system which had in fact developed regarding the closing of the bow doors.

Although he, Mr Stanley, was nominally in charge of closing the doors there was no system whereby he was the only person responsible. He was not the only person who ever closed them and they were often closed by other crew members . . . [It was] a very sloppy system and on the voyages on which he was engaged on maintenance, Mr Stanley often did not shut the bow doors. We must be careful not to allow the weight of this tragedy to fall on the unsupported shoulders of the assistant bosun.

The system of checking if the bow doors had been shut devolved on the loading officer who, on the *Herald*, was the chief officer, Mr Leslie Sabel. But, as Mr Steel pointed out, the regulations under which the ferry was operating required him to be in two places at once – checking the bow doors and taking up his position on the bridge for 'Harbour Stations'. Concern was expressed about the veracity of Sabel's evidence and the differing statements he made afterwards although, as the inquiry report states, due allowance should be made for his mental and physical condition at the time. The report found, however, that whatever the version of what happened, Mr Sabel had 'failed to carry out his duty to ensure that the bow doors were closed. He was seriously negligent as a result of this failure'.

Mr David Steel, QC, also pointed out that instructions for closing the bow doors of one of the *Herald's* sister ships, the *Pride of Free Enterprise*, did not include a single reference to an assistant bosun being responsible for closing the doors, nor did they mention that a loading officer (in this case the chief officer) should supervise such an operation.

The issue then took on a whole new dimension when Mr Steel began to cross-examine Mr Jeffrey Develin, a director of Townsend Car Ferries. Giving evidence on 7 May, he had told the investigation that he had first considered installing lights on the bridge of ferries to indicate whether or not the bow doors were closed, the day after the disaster. On 11 May, however, according to *The Times*, 'he broke into tears' as he denied having sought to mislead the inquiry (a more robust report in the *Guardian* of the same date noted he had 'lied'). He would have been hard put to say anything else since by that time the investigation had heard evidence of the number of times warning lights had been suggested.

Concern first arose in October 1983 when the assistant bosun of the *Pride of Free Enterprise* neglected to close both the bow *and* the stern doors before sailing, and he too was said to have fallen asleep. On 6 October 1983 the master of the *Pride* sent a circular to all deck officers, bosuns and assistant bosuns noting that twice since going on the Zeebrugge run, the ship had sailed with stern or bow doors open. He put it down to continual crew changes but pointed out the dangers of the situation and ordered crews to give it their utmost attention.

On 28 June 1985 Captain Blowers of the *Pride* wrote a memorandum to Mr Develin in which, among other things, he pointed out that there was nothing to indicate on the bridge whether or not the bow doors were closed. 'With the very short distance between the berth and the open sea this can be a problem if the operator is delayed or having problems in closing the doors. Indicator lights on the very excellent mimic panel could enable the bridge team to monitor the situation in such circumstances.' Mr Develin replied on 10 July 1985, saying he would pass the comments on.

The answers from the top brass of Townsend Ferries are illuminating; or as Mr Justice Sheen put it, 'quite shocking'; or as *The Times* described them on 12 May 1987, 'fatuous'. J. F. Alcindor, a deputy chief superintendent had said: 'Do they need an indicator to tell them whether the deck storekeeper is awake and sober? My goodness!' From Mr A. C. Reynolds, 'Nice – but don't we already pay someone?' From Mr R. Ellison, 'Assume the guy who shuts the doors tells the bridge if there is a problem', and from Mr D. R. Hamilton, 'Nice!'

'It is hardly necessary', comments the report, to point out that these replies display an absence of any sense of responsibility. If serious consideration had been given to this suggestion back in 1985, 'it is at least possible that they would have been fitted in the early months of 1986 and this disaster might well have been prevented'.

Captains continued to raise the matter. On 17 May 1986 Captain J. Kirby, senior master of the *Herald* sent a memorandum about it to Mr Alcindor and on 9 October in the same year Captain de Ste. Croix sent another, this time to the senior electrical officer, as 'another incident' had reminded him of his original request that warning lights be fitted on the bridge. 'Is the issue still being considered', he inquired, 'or has it been considered too difficult or expensive?'

A note on the memorandum says the request should be submitted on the usual application form and 'if it receives their [the marine department's] blessing I will proceed with the specification. It can be done, but will require a few deck and bulkhead penetrations.' On 13 October 1986 Captain de Ste. Croix submitted a job specification in these terms: 'Bridge indication is required to show whether the G. deck bow and stern w/t doors are in the secure or insecure mode.' On this Mr Alcindor wrote: 'Please write up preliminary specification for pricing.' On 18 October Mr R. W. King sent a memo back to him saying, 'I cannot see the purpose or the need for the stern door to be monitored on the bridge as the seaman in charge of closing the doors is standing by the control panel watching them close'.

Mr Alcindor duly replied to Captain de Ste. Croix saying, 'I concur in part with Mr King's penultimate paragraph that the project is unnecessary and not the real answer to the problem.' So long as somebody made sure the bow doors were closed and as the stern doors were clearly visible 'the problem should not arise. So in conclusion the Bridge indication is a "no go".'

Still undaunted, Captain de Ste. Croix wrote yet again to all the masters stating he considered bridge indication was required for both bow and stern doors 'due to their extreme importance'. He asked if he could have their opinion – if they all agreed that it was necessary, and did they think it would be expensive?

Faced with all this it is not surprising Mr Develin burst into tears. It was obvious, as the report points out, that by the autumn of 1986 the shore staff of the company were very well aware of the possibility that one of their ships would sail with her stern or bow doors open. They were also aware of

a very sensible and simple device in the form of indicator lights which had been suggested by responsible Masters. That it was a sensible suggestion is now self-evident from the fact that the Company has installed indicator lights in their ships. That it was simple is illustrated by the fact that within a matter of days after the disaster, indicator lights were installed in the remaining *Spirit* class ships and other ships of the fleet.

The way management treated the suggestion illustrated all too well the attitude of the marine department of the company to any suggestions made by masters. That was also shown by similar concerns expressed about overloading.

One of the reasons why the number of dead was underestimated initially was because the *Herald* was carrying more passengers than she should have been. During the subsequent cross-examination on this topic Mr Jeffrey Develin was to take centre stage again.

Before this happened, Captain Lewry, of the *Herald* had been asked about his ship's draught, as it is a legal requirement that the master should know what it is and that it be entered in the official log book before the ship is put to sea. He needs to know it because it restricts the number of passengers he can carry. This was vital at Zeebrugge as the ship had to be trimmed by the head to load the vehicles. Captain Lewry told the investigation quite frankly that no attempt had been made to read the draught of his ship on a regular basis or indeed at all in routine service. Fictitious figures were entered in the log book which took no account of having to trim the ship by water ballast. If the figures had been checked they would have shown the ship always sailing on an even keel although it normally left Zeebrugge trimmed (i.e. down somewhat) by the head.

On 24 October 1983 Captain Martin had written to Mr Develin pointing out problems in sailing with the ship down by the head. At full, or even reduced, speed the bow wave came three-quarters of the way up the bow door, the ship did not respond so well and 'you probably appreciate we never know how much cargo we are carrying so that a situation could arise that not only are we overloaded by 400 tons but also trimmed by the head by 1.4m. I have not been able to work out how that would affect our stability.'

Asked what he made of it, Mr Develin gave a variety of answers ranging from his thinking it was just an operational matter with which he was being acquainted, through 'I believed he was exaggerating' – (the report notes that Mr Develin made it clear that he thought every complaint was an exaggeration) – to the fact that he, Develin, could see nothing wrong with sailing trimmed by the head and that if Captain Martin had been that worried about it he should have come into my office and 'banged my desk'.

The report notes that Mr Develin is 'a Fellow of the Royal Institution of Naval Architects and had been a Government Marine Surveyor in Hong Kong and should, therefore, have appreciated the problem'.

The investigation next heard from Mr W. J. Ayers, a naval architect who was, at the time of the disaster, a director of the company. He was, says the report, 'verbose, rambling and at times misleading'. Note was taken of a memorandum sent on 20 July 1982 by Captain R. P. Blowers, senior master of the *Pride*, pointing out how difficult it was to read the draught which for record purposes was 'as often or not guesstimated'. He suggested automatic draught recorders.

The matter was brought to his attention again in February 1983 following the sinking of the *European Gateway*, after which a company internal inquiry was initiated. Captain Martin sent a report to Mr Develin which was read by Mr Ayers in which he again points out that the ship's draught is not read before sailing and that the entry in the log book is 'completely erroneous'; that it is not standard practice to inform the master how many passengers he can carry before sailing; the tonnage of cargo is not declared to the master before sailing; and that 'full speed is maintained in dense fog'. (Against that someone had written 'policy'.)

Questioned about this, Mr Ayers at first said he had investigated the issues raised 'somewhere in this period' but, in the light of further questioning, the report noted 'that answer is not accepted by the Court'.

On the question of carrying too many passengers it is evident that the company was warned again and again by no less than seven different masters. The senior master of the *Pride of Free Enterprise* sent a memorandum dated 16 August 1982 to Mr A. P. Young, who was operations director, with a copy to Mr Jeffrey Develin:

Passenger Numbers: I have to report that on several occasions in the past two weeks the vessel is believed to have been carrying passengers in excess of our passenger limit, i.e. 1305. Examples I have details of are as follows:

1 28.7.82   1200   Dover/Calais – excess of some 250 passengers.

2	6.8.82	1200	Dover/Calais – excess of some 40 passengers.
3	8.8.82	1515	Calais/Dover – excess of some 100 passengers.
4	15.8.82	1515	Calais/Dover – excess of some 171 passengers.

He appended proof from another officer and expressed concern as to the attitude of shore-based staff. He finished by saying that apart from the 'obvious moralities and swingeing penalties involved I am most deeply concerned lest idle gossip . . . should find its way to the media with all the damaging enquiries that would follow'. Mr Young's response was that he was amazed and annoyed by a suggestion made by the master that the only reason the passenger count was more accurate on his last trip was because the shore staff had been aware the crew were checking. 'Time and again we have made it clear that the counting of numbers of passengers on tickets may not agree with the actual head count for a variety of reasons.' He was annoyed by what he saw as the master's 'continual disbelief in the intentions and abilities of shore-based staff'.

Complaints by ships' masters continued. On 31 October Captain Pearson, in command of the *Spirit*, wrote to Mr Young saying that on the previous Friday he had twice sailed with too many people and that whilst accepting all the inherent difficulties in counting heads, 'it appears that all commercial drivers were excluded from the head count'. Could Mr Young please investigate this? The response was an evasive letter to another official saying Mr Young's intention was eventually to retain all tickets ashore, 'which would cut out the differences between head count and ticket count'. The report sees this as a suggestion that by retaining all tickets ashore it would not be possible for those aboard to find out whether there were more people on board than there were supposed to have been.

A meeting of concerned ships' masters followed and it is clear that throughout the following years they were becoming more and more alarmed. On 1 August 1986, just seven months before the sinking of the *Herald*, Captain de Ste. Croix wrote to Mr Young saying that he had learned he was carrying an extra 214 passengers. His original figure should have been 1,014, with the additional 214 this would make it 1,228 and 'way over the top'.

'As seeds of doubt had now been sown in my mind I decided to have a head count as they went off at Calais'. He found he was, in fact, carrying 1,682 passengers! 'This total is way over the life-saving capacity of the vessel. The fine for a Master for this offence is £5000 and probably confiscation of certificate. May I please know what steps the company intend to protect my career from mistakes of this nature?'

On 15 August Captain Stoker wrote complaining of carrying excess passengers. On 30 August Captain Martin sent a memorandum to Mr Young and Mr Develin saying that he had just done a voyage on which 1550 people were carried, 'the number of passengers over and above our certified number is clearly not acceptable and can only be described as a blatant and flagrant disregard of the system and backs up other complaints from Masters'. He asked that immediate steps be taken to remind shore staff of their responsibility. This prompted Mr Young to reply to the earlier letter from Captain Stoker saying that any system was liable to error but that the matter would be fully discussed. On 12 September 1986 Young received a letter from Captain Hartwell saying, 'I need not point out how serious this large discrepancy could be in an emergency to our integrity and efficiency if this sort of situation became public'. Prophetic words.

On 19 September Captain Ferrier carried an excess of 72 passengers, on 29 September Captain Martin carried an excess of 200. Both told Mr Young in writing. On 28 October a senior officer on the *Free Enterprise IV* wrote to Mr Young asking for an assurance that there would be a review of the system of counting heads.

He received a reply from Mr Cole dated 29 October 1986 which, notes the report, 'is illuminating'. The reason for the apparent overloading was 'that some stray tickets, that had to be put into the system somewhere, had in fact been added to the sailing which produced a false figure of 1200'. Mr Young, says the report, was asked about that statement. 'At first his answers were very evasive but eventually he agreed that the figure given in the manifest *was a false one*'. The court reluctantly concluded that Mr Young 'made no proper or sincere effort to solve the problem'. He was unwilling to accept the figures given to him by no less than seven masters.

The Court takes a most serious view of the fact that so many of the Company's ferries were carrying an excessive number of passengers on so many occasions. Not only was it illegal for the excess passengers to have been carried, but it was also dangerous. It should not have been beyond the wit of the managers to devise a system which would have insured that the correct number were carried.

Another complaint laid at the door of Townsend was the frequent changing of crews. Captain Kirby, one of the five masters who took it in turn to command the *Herald*, wrote to Mr M. Ridley, chief superintendent of the company, on 22 November 1986, four months before it sank, taking up this point.

Many of the transient officers are here only for a few duties and in these circumstances their main concern is to get the ship loaded and safely between Dover and Calais. Although they are generally good officers it is unrealistic to expect them to become involved in checking the installations and equipment or the detailed organisation of this particular vessel which they do not regard as their own . . .

He returned to the theme on 28 January 1987 – five weeks before the ship sank – in a further memo to Mr Ridley saying he wished to stress again 'that the *Herald* badly needs a *permanent* complement of good deck officers. Our problem was outlined in my memo of 22 November. Since then the throughput of officers has increased even further, partly due to sickness'. Between 1 September and 28 January there had been 36 deck officers attached to the ship, they had lost two masters and gained one. 'To make matters worse the vessel has had an unprecedented seven changes in sailing schedule. The result has been a serious loss in continuity. Shipboard maintenance, safety gear checks, crew training and the overall smooth running of the vessel have all suffered . . .' Note the comment about safety gear checks.

Finally there is the question of the turnaround. Why, the investigation had asked, had the loading officer/chief officer had to rush up to the bridge and not remain on the loading deck? Why was there such evidence of rush? The court found some difficulties in finding a clear answer.

But the sense of urgency to sail at the earliest possible moment was exemplified by an internal memorandum sent to assistant managers by Mr D. Shipley, operations manager at Zeebrugge. It is dated 18 August 1986.

> There seems to be a general tendency of satisfaction if the ship has sailed two or three minutes early. Where a full load is present then every effort has to be made to sail the ship *fifteen minutes* [my italics] early . . . put pressure on the first officer if you don't think he's moving fast enough. Have your load ready when the vessel is in and marshall your staff and machines to work efficiently. Let's put the record straight, sailing late out of Zeebrugge isn't on. It's 15 minutes early for us.

Mr Young tried to explain away that memo, says the report, on the basis that the language was used merely for the purposes of what he called 'motivation'. But it was entirely in keeping with his own thoughts at the time for he himself had endorsed the view in a memo he sent to Captain Thorne, senior master of *Free Enterprise VIII* in August 1986.

In summing up, the report says that 'at first sight' the faults which led to the disaster were the errors on the part of the assistant bosun, chief officer and master.

> But a full investigation into the circumstances of the disaster leads inexorably to the conclusion that the underlying or cardinal faults lay higher up in the Company. The Board of Directors did not appreciate their responsibility for the safe management of their ships. They did not apply their minds to the question: What orders should be given for the safety of our ships? The directors did not have any proper comprehension of what their duties were.

This was apparent during the cross-questioning of both Mr A. P. Young and Mr W. J. Ayers. 'The Court was singularly unimpressed with these gentlemen.'

The decision of the court was that the capsizing of the *Herald of Free Enterprise* was partly caused or contributed to by the serious negligence in the discharge of their duties by Captain David Lewry (master), Mr Leslie Sabel (chief officer) and Mr Mark Victor Stanley (assistant bosun) and partly caused or contributed to by the fault of Townsend Car Ferries. Captain David Lewry had his certificate suspended for a year and Mr Sabel for two.

Aftermath

It is hardly surprising, therefore, that the inquest on the dead returned the rare verdict, in such cases, of Unlawful Killing. As a result of this the Director of Public Prosecutions asked Kent police to investigate whether Townsend and its managers could be held responsible. At the time of writing, eighteen months after the tragedy, the increasingly bitter families of the victims are still awaiting the result of the police inquiries. The DPP has examined the papers from the Sheen Investigation and the inquest and, says the Herald Families Association, if the DPP decides not to launch a prosecution of the company, then the association will feel bound to bring a private prosecution.

As the *Daily Telegraph* said in its editorial on 10 October 1987, 'If the DPP cannot surmount the difficulty of bringing the company to book, relatives may well feel impelled to attempt a private prosecution. It would be shameful if they were driven to that.'

The Sheen Report does make it clear that P & O, Townsend's new owners, quickly replaced the company's entire management structure and rushed through a comprehensive shake-up of management procedures. The report recommended immediate changes such as passengers' boarding cards so that the exact number of passengers being carried was known, installation of indicator lights to show whether doors are closed and the use of closed circuit television to monitor all external doors. It also wanted consideration given to phasing out any vessels that were built under earlier regulations if they cannot meet, or be modified to meet, at least the 1980 regulations for passenger ferries. We will look in a later chapter at what many experts consider to be the inherent vulnerability of Ro-Ro ferries in general.

The government has rushed through a new Merchant Shipping Act and has also pushed for changes at the International Maritime Organization. From October 1989 all

IMO members' new ships will have to have door indicator lights, TV monitoring of the vehicle deck and supplementary emergency lighting.

Meanwhile, as already noted, P & O are still waiting to know whether or not they are likely to face charges connected with the *Herald* disaster while the Kent police wrestle with the law of corporate responsibility. Sir Jeffrey Sterling, P & O's chairman, has stated on many occasions that he sees no reason for such a prosecution, but then, one might say he would, wouldn't he?

The company also engaged in a punishing dispute with members of the National Union of Seamen, who were extremely unhappy at the findings of the Sheen Investigation which named seamen and punished them but which could ensure no such sanctions against management. Early in 1988 P & O announced swingeing cutbacks in its staff and altered its shift-work patterns for economic reasons. This brought about a walkout at Dover. The NUS supported the Dover strikers and other ports came out in sympathy over what they saw, primarily, as a matter of safety; but, under the present trade union legislation, this was not considered legal activity and the NUS had its assets sequestered until such time as it ceased to support the Dover men. P & O fired the Dover strikers and brought in new crews, thus enabling them to continue sailing, but the dispute had cost them from £20–£30m between February and August 1988, according to marine economists, and had sunk the company's half-yearly profits (*Guardian*, 15 August 1988).

Meanwhile, stories coming from the new crews are not exactly reassuring. One, in the form of an affidavit sworn on 21 July 1988, is from John Douglas Ball who was taken on by P & O in May 1988 as a motorman on the *European Clearway*, a passenger ferry operating on the Zeebrugge–Dover run.

He joined the merchant service in 1977 and has worked all over the world with the rank of chief petty officer. His past record of conduct with respect to safety matters won him the award of 'Safety Sailor of the Year' by Shell Tankers (UK) Ltd. and he also holds a campaign medal won ironically, while, on the P & O-owned *Canberra* during the Falklands War.

In the early hours of the morning of 16 July while the *European Clearway* was at sea, a major fire broke out in the engine room.

The beginnings of the fire, he says in his affidavit, went back four weeks when he had noticed that a leak had appeared in a hydraulic pipe which ran immediately above the starboard main engine exhaust. The pipe carries oil which is normally maintained under pressure and the system was pressurized when the leak appeared.

When the leak was noticed, the system was shut down so it could be repaired. In the meantime a bucket was tied up under the leak to catch any further drips of oil. Such a measure was obviously, he says, an extremely temporary one and he assumed the pipe would be repaired within the next couple of days.

During the night, walking past the main engines he saw what he describes as 'a wall of flame some ten feet wide stretching from the top of the engine up to the deckhead or ceiling'. He immediately returned to the control room and informed the second engineer before making any attempt to tackle the fire on his own. The second engineer triggered the engineers' alarm, an alarm local to their cabins, informed the bridge and shut off the engine. Mr Ball took a dry powder extinguisher and tackled the fire which was controlled within 45 seconds.

Once the fire had been put out its cause was obvious. The bucket, rigged up earlier, was still in place catching oil dripping from the leaking pipe. He was, he says, 'astounded to discover that this was the case'. Furthermore, 'to my astonishment and horror, it was apparent that the pressure in the hydraulic system had been turned back on, although the leak had not been repaired. The bucket had simply filled up and overflowed and the hydraulic fluid had poured on to the starboard exhaust, resulting in the fire.'

The next day he checked out the ship's general alarm system, as distinct from the engineers' local one, as it had not sounded during the fire. He discovered that the alarm system had been switched off. As a result, the passengers, and indeed most of the crew, were unaware that a fire had ever taken place. It had, he said, been known before he went on leave that the engine room alarm had been switched off because of a faulty alarm sensor which had not been repaired but he had assumed that, too, had been put right. Had it been working it would have been triggered off at the first hint of fire, thus alerting the bridge and bringing in firefighters. As it was, it was pure chance that he was where he was when he saw the fire.

> Given the location of the fire in the engine room, and the close presence of fuel and oil and the fact that the ship was in the middle of crossing one of the busiest sea lanes in the world, I can only conclude that a disaster of appalling proportions was narrowly averted.

Nor was this all. On his last tour of duty he had noted that both engines were severely overheating to the extent that the exhaust 'was burning cherry red'. Two days later, as the ship neared Zeebrugge, some of the casing bolts on the exhaust side of the turbo-chargers snapped off. The result was that out of an original 24 bolts on each engine, only 9 were left on the port engine and 13 on the starboard by the time the ship reached Zeebrugge. He was sure this was due to the overheating he had seen and reported.

At Zeebrugge it was decided to do the return journey, using only one engine at reduced speed. 'I consider this unwise and unsafe.' On reaching Dover the port engine was repaired, taking some thirty hours, but not the starboard, and the ship returned to service with the damaged engine being used on full power until it was finally repaired.

He decided to tell his story to the press and was immediately brought under extreme pressure to drop the matter. He was accused by a P & O official of lying. 'However I refused to bow to his pressure to alter any aspect of my story which is all entirely true.' He finally told it again to Mr Jenkinson of the Department of Transport who, he says, commended both him and the second engineer for the way they tackled the fire and for keeping their heads.

Another fire story came from Russell Tricky, a steward on the company's *European Trader*, who was refused permission by the Attorney-General to bring a private prosecution against P & O on the grounds that firefighters were unable to start tackling a fire which broke out earlier in the year because two oxygen cylinders for breathing apparatus were empty and had not been replaced. He also swore that the Department of Transport inspectors cleared the ship for sailing after watching a mishandled lifeboat launch which nearly put a man over the side. The company has described these incidents as 'absolute nonsense'.

In August 1988 came claims that P & O had allowed one of its freight ships to sail from Zeebrugge to Dover with its bow doors secured only by ropes and wire. An NUS spokesman said the incident was reported by a crewman who claimed the ship had sailed after emergency repairs had been carried out when locking pins failed.

The memorandum quoted at the beginning of this chapter also has some of the hallmarks of those read out during the Sheen Investigation. The memo, dated 8 July 1988 from Mr M. Chaston to all crews on all vessels, and with copies to management, points out that for £3.40 per head per annum staff can be covered for legal expenses in pursuing death and/or personal injury claims; free legal advice and 'defending criminal prosecutions, Health and Safety, leaving bow doors open, etc.' – which is, to say the least, tasteless. It is little wonder then that, according to a report in the *Guardian* (15 August 1988), P & O is so concerned about its image that it has commissioned market research to test the impact that its dispute with the seamen has had on other areas of its business, like Bovis homes and its luxury cruises and North Sea ferry operations.

The story of the *Herald of Free Enterprise* has been told in such detail because it is a classic example of an accident which was just waiting to happen.

So it was that in these thrusting, efficient and competitive times, when the 'enterprise culture' is held up as the example we should all follow, the aptly named *Herald of Free Enterprise* sailed against a background of complacency, cost cutting and the need to carry as many people as possible as quickly as possible to make the maximum possible profit.

For months and years, Townsend Car Ferries had been sailing ships where their masters had no idea of the depth of water they were drawing or of the weight of the cargo on board and where fictitious returns had been regularly entered. They had been sailing ships overloaded with passengers, contravening every rule in the book. There had been no continuity of crews. Every effort had to be put into faster and faster turnarounds until sailing fifteen minutes early was considered the norm. For whatever reasons, the constant and urgent requests for warning lights to double check that bow and stern doors were closed had been ignored.

All this was allowed to happen because, apart from the earlier 'mishap' with the *European Gateway*, nothing had gone wrong. All it took then was one young sleepy assistant bosun and the whole crumbling system fell apart – with the loss of nearly 200 lives.

3 King's Cross

> God gave Noah the rainbow sign,
> No more water, the fire next time.
>
> Negro spiritual

> As our hands touched I could feel his skin was red hot and some
> of his skin came off in my hand.
>
> Anthony Palmer, *survivor*

The fire started undramatically. About 6.30 p.m. on the evening
of 14 November 1987 commuter John Hickson, on his way home
to Peckham, saw some smoke and smelled burning rubber. He
reported it to a booking clerk. Twenty minutes later the two gates
between the Piccadilly and Metropolitan lines were locked,
following normal practice once the worst of the evening rush
hour had passed, which it had – just.

At approximately 7.15 p.m. a trainee legal executive, Angela
Campbell, smelled smoke at the top of the escalators and, as she
was later to describe, saw what looked like a black oily cloth
wrapped around something smouldering.

Fifteen minutes later Debbie Wren, a young secretary, saw
flames below the wooden slats on the Piccadilly escalator. As she
told the inquiry:

> When I was about halfway up I looked down at my feet. There
> were jets of smoke coming out from the gaps between the
> escalator steps. I could see a big orange glow underneath the
> escalator. I started to push the people in front of me. I thought
> about pushing the emergency button to stop the escalator but I
> didn't know whether that was the right thing.
>
>   I couldn't find a guard at the top of the escalator so I had to go
> to the other side of the concourse where there was a man sitting in
> a little box. I tapped on the window of the box. It took him a little
> while to understand what I was saying and then he got up to
> move and I left to catch my train.

Just one hour after John Hickson had reported the smoke and the smell of burning – at 7.30 p.m. – the Metropolitan police received their first 999 call. Stephen Hanson, a British Transport policeman, told the inquiry how he tried to stop people using the burning escalator. 'I was shouting "go back down, go back down". I was running around. I was hoarse. I was swallowing smoke and fumes.'

One minute later, BBC producer Judith Dingley, saw smoke coming out of the upward escalator. She did her best to stop people getting on to it and said, 'I stood there with my arms out like Jesus on the cross, saying "Don't go up, there's smoke". But nobody stopped. They just pushed past me and some people glared at me. I stood there for about half a minute with all these people pushing past and then I thought I'm getting out while I can and I went towards the platform.'

Four minutes later, at 7.35 p.m., a young estate agent from Potter's Bar, Guy Woolgrove, arrived at the station by tube. 'I got on to the escalator and there must have been about 150 people on it.' He was two-thirds of the way up when he said there was a 'whoosh' and heat came from everywhere.

I could feel the heat on the back of my neck but I didn't know where it was coming from. Somebody screamed and shouted, then everybody started screaming.

There was smoke everywhere, white smoke, then thick, black horrible smoke. It was pandemonium. Some people were falling back down the steps and landing on top of others. Somebody grabbed hold of my arm, everyone was linked together trying to climb up. We got on our hands and knees, it was easier to breathe down there. Somehow we managed to crawl to the top. Some people just couldn't get off the escalator. I saw the agony on one man's face. He tried to run up the escalator. It was moving then and he stumbled and knocked his head on the escalator steps and then tried to get himself up by putting his hands on the railing. But by this time the rubber on the railing was burning. I'll never forget the look on his face.

At the top there were groups of people doing nothing to help. There was some guy just standing there eating a bloody hamburger – it was evil.

Anthony Palmer, a Sheffield company director, who tried to drag two badly burned passengers to safety, told the inquest in October 1988 what happened when he approached one of them:

> As our hands touched I could feel his skin was red hot and some of his skin came off in my hand. I helped him out and when I was sure he was breathing I went back to help the people I could hear shouting and screaming inside the Underground.
>
> At the top of the stairway there was a woman, semi-crawling, obviously injured. I put my arms around her neck and assisted her. She was vomiting, coughing, choking on blood.

The woman was Rosalind Leech, a secretary from Hatfield. She told the inquest: 'I really thought I was a gonner. I had a little word with God and said, "I don't want to die yet, it isn't fair".' Richard Bates, a *Guardian* journalist who wrote most movingly afterwards about the fire which badly burned his hands and from which he had been saved by a then unknown person, described how he saw the 'flashover' of the fire at the top of the escalator. 'As I started to move forward I heard a large whooshing noise and saw a wall of flame which reached from floor to ceiling. I instinctively crouched down and put my hands before my face.' His clothes were set on fire as he ran through the dense smoke, throwing himself down another escalator. A man sprayed a fire extinguisher on him to put out the flames.

At 7.36 p.m. the London Fire Brigade logged alarm calls from the police, London Transport and members of the public. Euston firemen had been called out on a false alarm call to University College Hospital, so pumps were sent from Soho, Clerkenwell and Manchester Square under the command of Divisional Officer Cliff Shore.

The first fire engines arrived on the scene at 7.43 p.m., one hour and twelve minutes after the first suspicion that there was a fire. Station Officer Colin Townsley from Soho and sub-officer Bell from Clerkenwell went into the station concourse, by which time flames had reached the handrail on the escalator. Bell was to say later that it smelled like a rubbish fire. Townsley stayed in the concourse while Bell went below. Flames had now reached the ceiling of the shaft and he found some 200 people at the bottom of the escalator and on the platform.

Andrew Lee from St Albans had just got off a Northern Line train and he smelled smoke. With others he went towards the escalators. There was, he said, no sense of urgency. A policeman and fireman directed him to the steps which led to the Victoria Line escalator where a fireman was directing passengers. Halfway up 'a sheet of flame flashed across the shaft opening'. Police Constable Stephen Hanson, at the top of the escalator, said:

> A fireball just hit me in the face and in the hands. It knocked me off my feet. It was so dark that people were wandering around not knowing how to get out. I was trying to tell people to follow me. I knew where I was going but there was too much panic. I was on my hands and knees trying to keep below the fireball. I was shouting 'head for the wall'. You could see the balls of fire above your head, crawling along the ceiling.

At 7.45 p.m. a message came into the Transport Police control room that at least four people had been injured. The first ambulances were called and firemen threw ropes down exit stairs to pull survivors to safety. Lee and other passengers hurried back down the escalator and as a train pulled in on the Victoria Line, he and some other passengers got on to it.

As Divisional Officer Shore arrived to take control, Colin Townsley called for another pump. More ambulances were sent for. At 7.53 p.m. the fire was described as 'a major incident' and more fire pumps were requested. At 7.59 p.m. the first ambulance arrived. Just after 8 p.m., Divisional Officer Shore asked for twelve pumps. Later one fireman was to say that they didn't know where to go.

> I followed a hose with a colleague and found two firemen at the end of it in the concourse. There were some bodies. We left them, we were looking for live ones. The escalators looked like a volcano. There were sheets of flames around us. Ceiling tiles were falling on us. Every time a train went through the station the fire would roar up all over again.

Bodies were found in exit corridors, the ticket hall and at the top of the escalators. Firemen were about to put a cloth over one 'dead' body when it stirred into life.

At 8.09 p.m. the ambulance service declared Kings Cross a 'major incident' and called in reinforcements, advising University College and St Bartholomew's Hospitals to go on to 'Red Alert' (which means that all beds must be kept for emergencies only). Consultants, doctors and nurses in casualty units were alerted and the departments cleared. Off-duty staff were called in and the first ambulance left King's Cross.

Eleven casualties were taken to University College. More people were known to be trapped down below. Finally two escalator engineers reached the machine room below the booking hall while fire raged over their heads. They cut off the machinery.

By 8.20 p.m. there were calls for twenty pumps at King's Cross, while at UCH a plastic surgeon, Michel Brough, began operating on 'the worst flashburns I've ever seen'. By 8.22 p.m. the ambulance men told their control that all the surviving casualties had been found. Twenty minutes later Station Officer Colin Townsley was carried out of the station in a collapsed state. He was found to be dead.

More pumps arrived from as far afield as Millwall and finally there were 200 firemen on the scene. At 11.32 p.m. the first estimate of the dead was announced – thirty-two. Transport Minister Paul Channon then arrived at King's Cross. At 12.12 a.m. University College Hospital signalled that it was stretched to the limit and could accept no more victims. At 1.30 a.m. the death toll was confirmed at thirty, with eleven people seriously injured and nine less so. Most of the injuries were severe burns and one other man was later to die of his.

At 1.42 a.m. – seven hours and twelve minutes after John Hickson alerted the booking clerk, the fire was finally put out.

If ever a disaster was waiting to happen it was the King's Cross Fire. King's Cross is the busiest underground station on the world's oldest and most extensive underground railway system.

In 1984, after the government had abolished the Greater London Council, London Regional Transport was created by the London Regional Transport Act and began its operations in June of that year. The underground part of the operation became a subsidiary company called London Underground Ltd.

In his letter of 20 July 1984 to the chairman of London

Regional Transport, the then Secretary of State for Transport, Nicholas Ridley, set out the aims and tasks of the new organization. There were four. One was to improve services 'within the resources available'; the second was '*to reduce* costs [my italics], including fraud, and the call on taxpayers' and ratepayers' money'; the third was to involve the private sector more in the provision of services; and the last was to promote better management. Nowhere in the document was safety mentioned.

The new London Regional Transport (LRT) under the chairmanship of Sir Keith Bright, and London Underground Ltd. under Dr Tony Ridley, its chairman and managing director, appear to have set about part, at least, of their task with a will, especially with regard to the second aim. London Underground was to reduce its subsidy from the government from £190m to £90m in three years – something unheard of in any other similar system in the world – and so enthusiastically was the aim carried out that it was actually over-achieved.

London Transport operated, as John Hendy, QC, representing the Association of London Authorities was to say at the subsequent inquiry, in 'a cold climate', making 'desperate efforts to save money'. The new, stringent financial objectives set by Nicholas Ridley had not mentioned safety, only that it should manage with a diminishing subsidy each year. The strict financial regimen imposed on the system was 'all part of a financial atmosphere where safety does not merit a mention. Cuts in the budget had been felt throughout the system and financial restraints had dominated decision-taking which led to desperate efforts to save money.'

There was, in fact, no shortage of warnings of the hazards of the system. The company's chief fire inspector reported in early 1987 that 'the same fire hazards are found year after year in escalator machine rooms – and fire safety standards are gradually deteriorating'. He added, 'It seems very little consideration is given to fire precaution'.

He was later to tell the inquiry that his report had been 'ignored' and that his superiors 'did not regard his department as very important'.

Seven months before the fire the Railways Inspectorate –

which have themselves, subsequently, been heavily criticized – reported that 'standards of maintenance were declining with alarming rapidity' and listed dozens of faults and bad safety practices in many London stations.

The maintenance budget for lifts and escalators was planned to fall from £9.8m in 1986–7 to £7.2m in 1990–1 at a time when there was more pressure on the system than ever before. The wooden escalator where the fire started had caught fire twice in the days before the disaster, the inquiry was to learn. It had been installed 48 years previously and had a history of mechanical problems and endless need for repair. It was patched up after the fires on 7 and 11 November. Later, at the inquest in 1988, it was admitted that it had caught fire no less than 18 times in the run up to the King's Cross fire.

Between 1958 and 1987 there had been over 400 serious underground fires and many others which were less so. Students of the English language familiar with the arguments on post-structuralism and de-structuralism will be intrigued to know that fires were not referred to as fires but as 'smoulderings'!

There were at least two recent major incidents from which lessons could have been learned. In 1984 there was a serious fire at Oxford Circus station after which smoking was banned on the trains themselves. But a large number of other safety recommendations were not carried out. In June 1987 there was a fire at Green Park station on a wooden escalator similar to that at King's Cross. It burst into flames towards the end of the evening rush hour and a large number of passengers blundered around blindly in the underground tunnels in thick black smoke. A report written by Mr Garry Brown, station foreman on the Metropolitan Line, was sent to the management of London Underground Ltd. but was not even acknowledged until *after* the King's Cross fire.

Later Mr Brown was to say: 'I was not invited to speak to senior London Underground Officers until after the King's Cross disaster. It is quite clear that there was a cover-up after Green Park and London Underground was deeply embarrassed.' In October 1987 he submitted a second report critical of staff training on fire fighting and on the mechanics of escalators and lifts. 'Station staff in general are not taught the correct procedure in extinguishing or controlling a fire, be it only small.'

He recommended more stringent training on fire fighting, and on evacuation of stations. More staff of a higher calibre were needed. Station staffs' requests for the removal of rubbish were often ignored by the authorities and inflammable materials were regularly stored underground. He asked for the establishment of an independent body to review standards of staff training on a permanent basis. The response of Mr Terry Andrews, the authority's general manager was, according to a report in *The Times* of 19 February 1988, that Mr Brown's reports were 'exaggerated'.

Yet what he said was, with hindsight, extremely pertinent, for the Green Park fire mirrored closely the situation which was to obtain at King's Cross. The first sign was smoke, then small flames, which rapidly grew to two feet in height. Mr Brown and a colleague could not turn on the sprinkler system as 'it was switched off from the machine room which was locked. The station supervisor who had the key could not be found. Passengers were still using the other escalator and no one was stopping them at the top.' The flames reached a height of 3 feet and trains were told to go straight through the station – which they did at a much faster speed than recommended thus displacing air and fanning the flames, with each drawing more smoke down from the fire on to the platform area.

Mr Brown's fears were borne out by the Annual Fire Inspection of 'Deep Tube Lines and Stations' by the London Fire Brigade in the October before King's Cross. On virtually every single station inspected, mention is made of piles of inflammable rubbish, grease and rags, and again and again there is mention of combustible material in and around escalators or in their machine rooms.

You can pick almost any station at random.

Waterloo Oil containers stored in close vicinity of escalator No. 1, motor and plastic container of waste oil by escalator No. 2, must be removed ... Large wooden box of escalator parts, panels and cable drum must be removed from entrance to escalators 7 and 8 ... defective hose reel in escalators 7 and 8 to be repaired ... accumulation of rubbish ... accumulation of litter ... rubbish to be cleared from bottom of the ventilation shaft ... oil and sawdust must be cleared from floor of relay room ...

Bond Street Paper sacks, rags and rubbish must be removed from rear of circuit breakers and polythene bags of oily rags also removed from No. 6 and No. 8 escalators machine room ... rubbish to be cleared from invert sited at the lower chamber of escalators 3, 4 and 5 ...

As has already been noted there had been an extremely serious fire at Oxford Circus only three years before but the Fire Brigade inspectors could still report:

Oxford Circus Sacks of rubbish and escalator's treads must be removed from entrance to nos 11–14 escalators machine room ... sacks of rubbish must be removed from No. 1 and No. 6 escalators machine rooms and also from room sited at the top of No. 6 escalator ...

Chancery Lane Contractors rubbish must be cleared from No. 4 and No. 5 escalators machine room and sacks of rubbish removed from lower chamber of Nos 2 and 3 escalators ...

Ninety-two stations were inspected. Of these, it was stated in forty-one cases that there was inflammable material either in the escalators machine rooms or on or near to the escalators which should be cleaned out. Where the stations had lifts, all too often, it is noted, there were large amounts of rubbish piled in or around lift shafts. Dirt, grease, rubbish, old pieces of equipment, piles of wood, building materials appear again and again in the report, along with defective lights, obstructed sprinkler heads and, every now and then, there is a mention of 'unsuitable means of escape.'

The report on King's Cross is given here in full.

King's Cross

Booking Hall:
Cardboard boxes of escalators spare parts must be removed from top of the stairs to 1, 2, 3 escalators machine room, and rags must

be stored in bin, rubbish, old treads and cardboard box of parts must also be removed from lower chamber.

All combustible materials must be cleared from contractors' store room sited at the top of 1, 2, 3 escalators.

Oil drums and polythene oil containers must be stored in bins 4, 5, 6, 7 escalators machine room, and old treads, cables removed from lower chamber.

Rubbish to be cleared from vent plant room floor.

Obstructions must be removed from entrance to vent plant room sited in ticket store, and ticket rolls must be stored properly.

Sprinkler heads in tenant shop (Heel Bar) to be cleaned.

Platforms:
Sacks of rubbish and cables must be removed from telephone exchange, platform 1 Northern Line.

Cable drum, cardboard box of lagging, cleaning materials, plaster boards must be removed from pump room Victoria Line.

Paraffin, grease and oil containers must be stored in bins, bucket of waste oil removed and missing ceiling tiles replaced in Per Way tool room Victoria Line.

Rubbish to be cleared from disused spiral stairs.

Accumulation of litter to be cleared from southbound Victoria and northbound Piccadilly Line tunnels.

Cable drum, loose cables, fittings and rubbish must be removed from disused signal cabin.

Paper bags, cardboard boxes, old uniforms must be cleared from top of lockers in staff locker room.

Yet it was against this background that the number of cleaners at King's Cross was reduced from fourteen to two.

Amazingly enough it was not possible for the Fire Brigade to bring any pressure to bear on London Underground Ltd. Under present legislation, through a quirky loophole in the law, it is not possible for them to issue fire certification as would be the case in almost any other public building. The Railways Inspectorate has the power to issue statutory notices requiring fire hazards to be removed and, according to Frank Dobson, MP, in whose constituency King's Cross is situated, 'informal warnings' were issued to some stations in May 1986 but no statutory notices were issued until after the King's Cross fire. 'But', he said, 'there's nothing unusual in that – they didn't issue a single notice in 1986 and only one in 1985.'

He was not happy that the Inspector of Railways was appointed to sit on the subsequent inquiry and revealed, in November 1988, that in fact only one inspector was actually in post during 1987 monitoring the whole of British Railways' Network South East *and* the whole of the London Underground system . . .

Mrs Thatcher, as is her custom following disasters, visited the victims in their hospital beds, looking as one unkind critic was to say, 'like the Grim Reaper'. Sir Keith Bright proffered his resignation to the then Secretary of State, Paul Channon, but this was refused. Questioned vigorously in November 1988 as to why it had not been accepted, Mr Channon said it was felt that Sir Keith would provide the necessary continuity while safety measures were put in hand.

It was announced that a full-scale public inquiry would be set up and on 23 November 1987 Mr Desmond Fennell, QC, was appointed to hold it. The speed with which the Zeebrugge investigation was held and its report published was not mirrored in this case. The report did not appear until November 1988, after the inquest and not before as was the case with Zeebrugge.

It is not possible to recite here the whole course of that inquiry but it quickly became apparent that the situation at King's Cross on that fatal night was absolutely chaotic. A great deal was made by management of the possibility of an arsonist who had deliberately started the fire but extensive police inquiries revealed no such cause. There was also talk of the possibility of the type of paint used on underground stations containing a component which had exacerbated the fire but this was also ruled out following extensive investigation.

The fire started, quite simply, because somebody dropped a lighted match on to an old escalator under which a horrifying half ton of combustible rubbish had been allowed to build up. Mr Jeffrey Styles, lift and escalator engineer for fourteen years, said 'it was a horrifying amount.' He told the inquiry that two and a half years before the disaster he had reported that skirting boards very close to the grease-filled tracks were of particularly flammable wood. Nearby wooden panels were also very flammable with a combustible varnish coating. The facts had been transmitted to the relevant departments but nothing had been done – nor had his other recommendations been acted upon, i.e. the relocation of 'water fog' sprinkler controls so they were not inaccessible, making the water fog system automatic, installing smoke detectors and replacing all wooden escalator parts and cleaning thoroughly all escalators. These recommendations were rejected at board and other levels of senior management, he told the inquiry.

The station, it turned out, had been allowed to 'go to sleep' after the evening rush hour. An acting station manager had made a tour of inspection an hour before the fire and had found nobody on duty on any of the tube platforms but had done nothing about it. Mr Charles Pugh, counsel for the victims, said of this that the station manager of London's biggest underground station 'was expected to discharge the responsibility of the captain of the ship with the powers of the cabin boy'. During the 45 minutes before the fire, passengers had been left entirely to their own devices on the six tube platforms and escalators.

An underground worker told the inquiry how unofficial triple-length meal breaks had become the norm and one said she might have been able to direct police unfamiliar with the station had she been at her post. Her colleague, a ticket collector, had joined her in her lengthy one-and-a-half-hour meal break and was known regularly to sleep during his long breaks and was often asleep in his ticket collector's box when he should have been checking tickets. At the time of the fire, only two ticket collectors had been working instead of five and there were no members of underground staff available, apart from those in the booking office, to evacuate passengers from the booking hall in the last minutes when this was still possible.

Those staff available were totally unprepared and untrained to cope with what happened. At the beginning of the emergency no attempt was made to stop people coming into the booking hall from the street and although two men did enter the escalator machine room no attempt was made to switch on the 'water fog' machinery. At 7.41 p.m. a call was made to order trains to go through the station without stopping, but this was not implemented for a crucial two minutes during which trains arrived and passengers got out, while others were still arriving in the booking hall.

The Fire Brigade arrived at 7.43 p.m. as has already been seen but only two minutes later the fatal flashover occurred which was to cause so many casualties. Right from the start firemen were hampered by the fact that no detailed plan of the layout of the station was available until an hour *after* the flashover and even then it was found to be inadequate.

Radio communication was poor or non-existent, and this also hampered the Transport Police when they arrived. Unaware of the position in the booking hall, they contunued to direct passengers up the escalators instead of evacuating them from the station by train. There were many, many other deficiencies. For example, one of the main exits had been locked once the rush hour was over, while fire-fighting equipment was 'hidden' behind building materials.

One of the most significant pieces of information to come out of the inquiry occurred on Day 73 when Dr Tony Ridley was asked about underground fires.

'You cannot regard fire as an acceptable hazard, can you? A fire is not an occupational hazard, is it?' asked Mr Fennell.

Dr Ridley's answer was: 'There are, and have been fires – or to use the euphemism, smoulderings, on London Underground year in and year out. They are part of the nature of the oldest, most extensive, most complex underground railway in the world. Anyone who believes that it is possible to act so that there are no fires ever, is I fear, misguided.'

The inquiry lasted 91 days and took evidence from 150 witnesses. Its findings were eagerly awaited, not least by the relatives of the victims and those who had been maimed in the fire. Ironically these included two professional guitarists who are unlikely ever to be able to play properly again – if they can play at all – as their hands were so badly burned. Some people suffered horrific facial injuries as well and have before them years of operations. All suffered the trauma now known to follow the experiences of those who have been involved in disasters.

As has already been pointed out, the Zeebrugge inquest took place after the publication of the report of the disaster, but this was not the case with King's Cross. Although there had been rumours since August 1988 that publication was imminent this was not so and it had still not appeared when the inquest began at the beginning of October 1988.

This took place in an atmosphere of bitter acrimony. London Transport had refused to pay the legal costs of the families of the victims to enable those who could not otherwise afford to be represented.

The coroner in the Zeebrugge inquest had directed the jury that they should not return a verdict of Unlawful Killing as this could only be based on the acts of an individual and not corporate negligence but, possibly fortified by the findings of the inquiry already published in the report, they did return such a verdict.

Remarkably, in this present case, it was to transpire that the Lord Chief Justice had directly intervened and informed the King's Cross coroner that such a verdict was not possible in the circumstances. The inquest had been expected to last weeks; in the event it lasted only days.

Accurate forensic evidence proved difficult, something explained in an article in the *New Scientist* (8 October 1988), but which has not been widely publicized. It pointed out that accurate identification of how each victim died was unlikely in the absence of an analysis of data, as there had been a mix-up of samples. The mix-up, by handlers of the blood samples, meant that the extracts could not each be related to particular bodies. Additionally, the two scientists who analysed the samples used two separate techniques. Opinions vary as to the reliability of the two.

So the inquest was unlikely to be able to determine the sources of the cyanide gases present during the fire. One possible source was melamine, the plastic widely used for surfacing the underground system. Firemen moved many bodies without noting the position of the corpses and consequently the siting of people who died with high levels of cyanide in their blood could not be established with any certainty.

If most of the victims had been near the ticket office which was clad in melamine, then it would have been possible to pinpoint melamine as the source of the toxic gases. Finally, although much of the material in the ticket hall and escalator burned during the fire, little was known about the timing of the combustion nor how long the victims survived. Some may have been knocked out by one set of fumes and then been unable to escape after inhaling another agent. No one knows if cyanide appeared early or late in the fire. Some victims had died from breathing hot gases or inhaling toxic fumes including carbon monoxide and cyanide. Some had lethal concentrations of one or the other in their blood.

Those who gave evidence and had to re-live their experiences became very distressed; one British Transport policeman, PC Stephen Hanson, broke down twice when he described finding one of the bodies.

Eventually London Transport agreed to pay the legal costs of the relatives of the victims but the only time they were called, on 10 October, was when the pathologist was unable to provide the jury with a correct list of names of the dead.

By 11 October the coroner was ready to sum up. Before he did so Matthew Scott, QC, representing the bereaved, said he felt that the jury had not heard the whole story and that they should do so, and he urged the coroner not to bar the verdict of Unlawful Killing. He referred in particular to the time it had taken before efforts were made to put out the fire and that there had been eighteen previous fires on that particular escalator.

The coroner, Dr Chambers, rejected Mr Scott's plea. He would, he said, be advising the jury that they could not return an Unlawful Killing verdict 'bearing in mind that the Lord Chief Justice has advised me to do this'; and, indeed, in his summing up he told the jury there was 'no place for a verdict of unlawful killing – it isn't that sort of court'.

He also said that he agreed with the coroner in the Gibraltar inquest (into the shooting of three suspected IRA terrorists earlier in the year by members of the SAS), that an open verdict should be avoided if possible. Accidental death was a verdict they could, however, bring 'with no hesitation whatsoever'. They did so after retiring at first for seventy minutes, and then for a further fifteen.

The feelings of the relatives of those who died were summed up in a letter to the *Guardian* on 14 October, written by Ms Sophie Tarassenko. She described the proceedings as 'farcical' and pointed out that the victims' relatives had been called merely to check out names.

The next day, the coroner's summing up was also full of 'surprises'; to mention but two: First we heard how the LRT area manager had gone under the escalator into the machine room and had indeed 'endeavoured to put out the fire'. Yet the man himself said last week that he had not used the fire extinguisher or the sprinkler system which were there, but merely gone in there, found a lot of smoke and come out again.

Secondly, a badly burned passenger would have been surprised to hear that he had been evacuated on a tube train, since we all heard last week that he had been taken out through the Midland Line exit – but only after a lengthy and frantic search for some keys to unlock it by LRT staff.

These were not the only inadequacies but what followed was really good theatre. The coroner, having offered the jury a choice of verdicts which amounted to one, sent them out to fill in 31 forms stating the cause of death, asphyxia, and details of victims, at the same time recommending that special mention be made of Mr Townsley's bravery.

Over an hour later, having returned, the jury were asked if they had completed these. The answer came from the Foreman: 'Accidental'. There was a pause. Had the forms been filled? The answer, hesitantly, came 'No'. The jury were sent out again, returning half an hour later with the forms filled. The coroner asked for the cause of death: asphyxia. Was there anything for the jury to add? 'No'. Silence. What about the special mention for Mr Townsley? Out marched the twelve again, followed by Dr Chambers who was saying that he would suggest a proper sentence for them to write. In they all came again a few minutes later. Did the jury want to add anything? Yes – and a sentence was read out by the foreman.

I fully endorse the statement about Mr Townsley's bravery and I go further – he died to save others and this has not been forgotten by any of us and never will be.

But I do question the integrity of the Inquest. I question the role of the jury who appeared to have no understanding at all of what they were doing there. I question their lack of choice as to verdict. I question the evident lack of accuracy in the coroner's summing up of the evidence. I question the verdict itself: why should the coroner feel obliged to write to London Regional Transport of his concern that this should never happen again if this was indeed a complete accident and therefore could never have been prevented?

This was indeed a farce about a tragedy. Nothing can bring back my brother but I feel that I and all the other families deserve better than this.

The report of the Fennell Inquiry was finally published on 10 November 1988. Counsel for the bereaved had tried to see an advance copy a week or two before but had been told nobody would do so until publication. In the event, senior LRT and London Underground Management did. On the evening of 10 November, Sir Keith Bright offered his resignation and this time it was accepted. On the morning of 11 November, Dr Tony Ridley followed suit in view of the findings of what he described as 'an emotive document'.

Some commentators contrasted the report favourably with that of Zeebrugge but this writer does not agree. It looks as if it contains more than the Zeebrugge inquiry report as it is the size of a telephone directory (and in appearance could be mistaken for one), is printed on glossy magazine paper with full colour illustrations, large type and three-inch margins on each page which make it look as if it has more content that it actually has. Unlike the Zeebrugge report it does not reprint copies of the warnings received by management prior to the disaster.

It is highly critical of senior management and this time the buck did not stop with some unfortunate low-level employee. Mr Fennell accepted that the concept of safety was 'enshrined in the ethos of railway operation' but it was clear they had a blind spot over the hazards of fire on escalators. In my judgement Mr Ridley was correct to say that 'London Transport at its highest level may not have given as high a priority to passenger safety in stations as it should have done'.

Nor did 'London Underground guard against the unpredictability of fires . . . since no one had been killed in earlier fires'. Government spokesmen were to make much of the fact that the findings of the report specifically mention that there is no evidence that cost cutting had affected safety or that economies had brought about the disaster; but the findings appear to contradict this since some of the earlier statements such as the fact that the only time the word 'safety' was mentioned in the context of the new aims for London Transport set by Mr

Nicholas Ridley was in the first aim which says 'to provide consistent with safety, the best value for money rail services within the resources made available by the pursuit of service quality, cost reduction and effective marketing'. (Ridley's letter of 20 July 1984 was not to mention safety at all.)

Mr Fennell noted that 'This is the only specific reference to safety in either the Secretary of State's objectives for London Regional Transport or in those of London Regional Transport for London Underground Ltd.'

The Fennell Report also said: 'It is apparent from the evidence given by the Chairman that whereas financial matters, namely productivity and budgeting, were strictly monitored, safety was not strictly monitored.' He had asked Sir Keith why, if independent guidelines had been set by which he could judge economy and efficiency was there difficulty about setting the same kind of independent guidelines which would have enabled the safety aspects to be properly considered. To this Sir Keith had replied: 'If I may pause a moment and try and give you the best answer I can ... (after a pause), I think the answer is that we did not approach it like that.'

'It is clear', wrote Mr Fennell, 'on the evidence of Sir Keith that his board did have proper regard to efficiency and economy; it is equally clear that they did not impose the same criteria when it came to safety operations.' Sir Keith, he said, had been in error in believing safety could be left to the subsidiary companies.

Dr Ridley had been 'struggling to shake off the blinkered approach' of the system's earlier history but he had remained convinced that fires were inevitable on the system. The approach of London Underground to passenger safety was reactive not pro-active and their reaction to warnings from earlier fires 'imperfect'

There was no system in place to ensure that the findings and recommendations of such inquiries were properly considered at the appropriate level. Many of the shortcomings in the physical and human state of affairs at King's Cross in 1987 had in fact been identified before by the internal inquiries into escalator fires.

They were also highlighted in reports by the Fire Brigade, police and Railway Fire Prevention and Fire Safety Standards Committee. The many recommendations had not been adequately considered by senior managers and there was no way to ensure they were circulated, considered and acted upon.

London Underground's failure to carry through the proposals resulting from earlier fires – such as the provision of automatic sprinklers, the need to ensure all fire equipment was correctly positioned and serviceable, identification of alternative means of escape, and the need to train staff to react properly and positively in emergencies – was a failure which I believe contributed to the disaster at King's Cross.

The Railways Inspectorate also came in for criticism. Mr Fennell said that they appeared to have 'misunderstood their duties' which led to 'a more relaxed approach with London Underground than they would otherwise have had. In my view, the Inspectorate in recent years has not made full use of its powers or devoted sufficient resources to London Underground to create the tension necessary to ensure safety', he wrote. Since, as we now know, only one inspector was responsible for both the London Underground and Network South East this is hardly surprising. However, there should have been 'more vigorous use of enforcement powers'.

Safety measures had been left in the hands of too many different people and specialist safety staff were usually of a junior level. 'Since no one had been killed in earlier fires London Underground Limited genuinely believed that with passengers and staff acting as fire detectors, there would be sufficient time to evacuate passengers safely.'

There had been no system to train staff either in fire drill or fire evacuation and it was not sufficient to have a policy based on fire precautions; fire prevention was necessary. There had been insufficient supervision and control of staff. When a station inspector went down to the escalator machine room he had been unable to get near to a small fire extinguisher and had actually passed the controls of the 'water fog system' but had made no effort to switch it on because he had never used it.

Communication was ineffective and there was none between those on each side of the station and those outside, and several opportunities for the vital exchange of information were lost. The Fire Brigade had not been called immediately, they had no detailed knowledge of the geography of the station, the

'Flashover' occurred only two minutes after they arrived and their chief fire officer was killed early on in the disaster.

There appeared to have been a breakdown in communication between the rescue services each pursuing their own duties but with a lack of liaison between them. Mr Fennell called for joint exercises between all the relevant services and the London Underground. The Transport Police could not be blamed for directing passengers up the escalators as they did not know what was happening above but 'one of the clear lessons for the Transport Police is the need for training in evacuation and communication, fire-fighting and incident control procedures as they apply to underground stations'. There were also problems in co-ordinating control with the ambulance service.

Even before the inquiry finished sitting, Mr Fennel had expressed his dissatisfaction with the '100 steps' on safety London Transport said they were taking in the light of the fire. After a private meeting with senior management he said the measures were inadequate and that a director with special responsibility for safety should be appointed.

He made 157 recommendations in the report. They included fitting escalators with heat detectors and machine rooms with smoke detectors, automatic sprinklers also to be fitted; there should be up-to-date plans of all stations available to London Fire Brigade and they should be consulted every time station alterations were planned; all wooden skirting boards and other panels must be replaced with metal by June 1989 and station staff must personally inspect all escalators every two hours until all wooden parts have been replaced; a wide number of steps had to be implemented connected with the management of safety and a non-executive director with responsibility for monitoring it should be appointed to the board. Safety must be the subject of audit.

Staff must be adequately trained with refresher training at regular intervals; public address systems and radio communications must be improved; the law regarding fire certificating by the Fire Brigade must be clarified; secondary methods of escape must be investigated; the Railways Inspectorate should be much more vigorous in its duties and the new underground ticketing system should be reviewed with advice from the Fire Brigade and Railways Inspectorate.

He did not find that economies or cutbacks in staff had been responsible for the King's Cross disaster but he was concerned that insufficient thought had been given to smoke detectors once there were not so many staff around to monitor stations – which is why he recommended they should be widely installed.

The government greeted the report with satisfaction, feeling that it had vindicated their view that the disaster had not been caused by economies and cutbacks of the underground system. Mr Paul Channon, invited to resign in the wake of Sir Keith Bright and Dr Tony Ridley, declined to do so.

Following Transport Secretary Paul Channon's statement to the House of Commons after the publication of the King's Cross report on 10 November 1988, he was specifically asked why he did not accept the resignation of Sir Keith Bright when it had been first offered. He was also asked why the word 'safety' had not appeared once in the letter from his predecessor, Nicholas Ridley, to London Transport setting out its aims and objectives.

He took the second question first and said that the Opposition spokesman had 'misrepresented my right hon. Friend's letter in which he set out the objectives of London Regional Transport. My right hon. Friend referred at the beginning of the letter to the Act setting out the framework of duties for the board and chairman of LRT. Safety is laid down as a paramount objective under section 2(2) of that Act.'

'There is no safety in that', responded shadow spokesman, John Prescott. Mr Channon repeated, 'The Act sets out the framework of duties'.

It is obvious that the government was expecting a question on the minister's earlier refusal to accept Sir Keith's resignation, and there was a carefully worded question from Tory backbencher Terence L. Higgins who suggested that was it not the case that Mr Channon had not accepted it because action was needed by the person familiar with the overall situation and that at that time there was no indication of the cause of the tragedy, to which Mr Channon replied, 'I entirely agree with my right hon. Friend. That is why I asked Sir Keith Bright to stay on. During the inquiry it was essential to have Sir Keith at the helm. That was the right course at the time.'

Questioned time and time again on the cutbacks in budgets, particularly for lifts and escalators, and the cutbacks in staffing levels, Mr Channon kept on quoting from the Fennell Report that 'in my judgement there is no evidence that the overall level of subsidy to London Regional Transport was inadequate to finance necessary safety-related spending and maintain safety-standards'.

The session was an arid one. To every question regarding finance and cutbacks, Mr Channon replied with the quote from Fennell which he was to repeat again throughout the evening on radio bulletins and television newscasts. In the House he was regularly 'questioned' by Tory back-benchers extolling the virtues of government policy and its generosity to public services in general and London Transport in particular. Reading the report in Hansard, one can only conclude that they never travel by London Underground.

The case against the government was probably best summed up by Dr John Marek, Labour MP for Wrexham, who said:

> Will the Secretary of State reflect on the fact that it demeans his office to try and brazen out a disaster of this kind and, like Pontius Pilate, to blame anyone but himself and his colleagues in the Government by giving misleading quotations, not quoting the report fairly, and seeking to introduce the superfluous question of capital investment, when 31 people died due to accumulated grease and debris which had nothing to do with capital investment? Does the Secretary of State accept that it was a matter of revenue expenditure and that those people died because of cuts in manning? I put this to him bluntly: has he asked, or will he ask, his right hon. Friend the Secretary of State for the Environment to consider his position? If not, there is no hole into which he will not crawl and no argument that he will not use to cling to office?

Aftermath

London Transport and London Underground Ltd. immediately announced that many of the recommendations suggested by Mr Fennell had been, or were being, implemented and that the situation regarding safety had much improved. Has it?

Since King's Cross there were, up to November 1988, twenty-one serious fires and numerous minor ones. The writer, who does not live or work in London, experienced two and, on the second occasion in October, was made with other panic-stricken passengers to remain on an overcrowded tube train and not get out at Warren Street station although the suspected fire was in the tunnel between Warren Street and Oxford Circus! Everyone using the system has seen the broken escalators (often deep in litter), and out-of-action lifts. London Underground admit that some fifty are likely to be not working at any one time.

Staff cuts continued and it is not unusual to come across a station with no staff in evidence there at all, not even ticket collectors or booking office clerks.

As has already been remarked, only one inspector had been responsible for checking both the underground system and Network South East for over a year and only three are responsible for all health and safety matters over that area, even when at full strength. The twenty-four strong staff of the Inspectorate have been busy advising on the safety of the Channel Tunnel, doing agency work for the governments of Hong Kong and Singapore, and negotiating for a contract with the Chinese government.

Most worrying of all, Fire Brigade Inspection reports on six stations including King's Cross and Euston found, once more, that there were still fire hazards, even if these were not on the scale of the previous report. (The 1988 report is printed in full in the Appendix.)

A report in BBC's *Newsnight*, transmitted on the night of the publication of the Fennell Report, contained interviews with staff who had still received no fire-drill training nor knew anyone who had, and with the driver of a one-man train who had driven into Wood Green station in May 1988 unaware that his train was on fire and when he did realize it, found there were no station staff around to assist him; the report also claimed that the Railways Inspectorate had told the BBC that it had been a deliberate policy not to carry out preventive checks on stations but declined to give a reason.

The BBC found confusing exit signs, no emergency exit signs, rubbish and flammable material piled up at Holborn station, more highly flammable rubbish behind a temporary hoarding near an old escalator at Bank station, and pieces of hardboard at the bottom of the lifts at Covent Garden.

The BBC, and also the *Guardian* (and anyone else who used it during the autumn of 1988) found bare wires hanging down from a half-completed ceiling at King's Cross. A notice said that London Underground was 'working round the clock' to get the work finished by the end of 1988. But, as the report said, 'with no sign of the new ticket machines and barriers, let alone the five new escalators planned, completion in seven weeks' time appears out of the question'. A mother bumping a pushchair down the narrow stairway to the King's Cross Piccadilly platform stopped all the traffic in both directions (with results which could only be imagined if there were to be an emergency), and at Covent Garden station the two new lifts still carry no more passengers than did the old one. Should a fire break out in this now very busy station, the only emergency exit up which the old, the feeble and women with babes in arms could go is a staircase of some 200 steps. Overcrowding on tube stations is now so bad that the Angel station has sometimes to be closed at peak hours due to congestion on its narrow, single platform.

A newer hazard is the latest form of ticket barrier, designed to try and stop people from avoiding paying their fares now that staff has been so reduced. It is narrow, shoulder-high, and made of concrete and you can only go through it by passing your ticket in whereupon it opens electronically. Frank Dobson, among many others, has underlined the hazard these would represent in the event of a fire. Other systems, such as the Paris Metro (which is large), and the Barcelona Metro (which is small), have gates designed to let people out fast should this be necessary. (The Paris Metro also holds frequent fire drills which include passengers too.)

But most chilling of all is the behind-the-scenes thinking, both before and after the disaster, which has leaked out during the last twelve months. Three weeks before the disaster, Mr Jeff Allen, the finance director of London Underground Ltd., circulated a memo to fellow executives detailing £4m worth of *mandatory* spending cuts – these included savings on Transport Police, train radios and, most significant of all, escalators.

The memorandum from Mr Allen, dated 30 October 1987, shows that some £570,000 of the proposed mandatory savings would mean some barriers are unattended 'with consequent risks of increased congestion and possibility of fraud'. A further £280,000 of overtime restrictions would bring 'some risk of failure to cover jobs' while a £40,000 saving on management training is described as a 'medium risk'.

The story was run by the *Observer* on 13 November 1988 but the LRT papers had already been circulating for some weeks because Mr Allen's paper appears to have had a direct bearing on what occurred at King's Cross, although the information is not contained in the Fennell Report. Although the closed circuit television link to line controllers' offices was considered to be 'very unreliable', £50,000 was cut from the budget for this and a further £360,000 removed from train radio enhancements along with £110,000 from the police radio system budget. One can only surmise what will happen now that better communications, especially radio links, are among the Fennell recommendations.

On the question of cameras and closed circuit television, it came out at the inquiry that they had not been working or working properly at the time of the fire. Mr Fennell said they had proved to be of no assistance during the fire.

The massive sum of £1m was to be taken off the budget for dealing with escalators. The cutbacks, said Mr Allen, had to be carried out to meet the new expenditure levels set by the board in line, as we have seen, with government policy for London Transport. 'You are directed to implement those which are appropriate to your area.'

More recent thinking is contained in a copy of a draft business plan drawn up by LRT managers, which came into the hands of Frank Dobson. This was written by Ms Judy Snell, senior corporate planner. On 18 August 1988 she complained that the plans for the year had been 'particularly poor on efficiency improvements, partly as a result of the need to spend more on safety. Business [that is the London Underground . . .] will be expected to put forward practical proposals to achieve unit cost reductions, bearing in mind the expected requirements for savings of three and a half per cent per annum.'

London Underground, in fact, should aim to break even by

1989/90 after various charges and unit cost reductions, something no similar system anywhere else would even contemplate. Both the tube and bus services should 'maintain a dynamic approach to seeking out such unit cost reductions while avoiding cuts which adversely affect quality of service,' which seems to be a contradiction in terms.

Ms Snell notes that plans could be upset by the findings of the Fennell Inquiry and says that some £110m had been put away in case LRT were forced by recommendations of the report to provide for the possibility of fire certification of all stations – but, as we have seen, the only recommendation is that the legal position should be clarified so it might well be that none of this money is spent on bringing the stations up to the standard required for a fire certificate.

It is also right to remember the praise heaped on the emergency services. In the light of that it should be noted that the London Fire Brigade has been told it has to make economy cuts, from £166m in 1988 to £142m in 1989. The London Ambulance Service has had its funds cut back so that at present ambulances get to 90 per cent of cases within fourteen minutes. The proper target is 95 per cent. (In some parts of the country this has been reduced to below 70 per cent.) Owing to NHS cuts University College Hospital, which took the brunt of the emergency, cannot open its new burns unit and is trying, in fact, to make still more cuts as it is expected to cut back expenditure by £5m by the end of 1988 and £4m by the end of 1989.

For many the long nightmare continues. Kwasi Afari-Minti has to wear a mask over his grotesquely disfigured face night and day to soften the skin in anticipation of years of plastic surgery operations. He was a guitarist but his fingers are now too weak and misshapen to play.

Richard Bates, a *Guardian* journalist who wrote movingly about his experiences after the fire and how his life had been saved by London fireman Peter Osborne was the man who, according to the coroner, had been rescued by evacuation on a train. In fact he had, as the letter from Ms Tarassenko pointed out, had to wait until someone found the keys to unlock the Midland Line exit gates. 'Twenty minutes of shouting, rattling and kicking the gates by the policeman as frightened and confused as me. I walked around in circles screaming with pain from my hands . . . I thought I was going to die.'

He, like other victims, is considering legal action. London Fire Brigade have already instituted proceedings. As Bates put it the day after the inquiry report was published:

I believe King's Cross was a disaster that need not have happened and that those 31 people died because those entrusted with the safety of London's public transport system abrogated their responsibility in the over-zealous pursuit of cash savings in an eagerness to please their political masters.

Worryingly I see no evidence that those same people have the commitment or the competence to make the Tube any safer in future. In takes more than the putting up of a few No Smoking signs to run a railroad.

Money has to be spent, not on automatic ticket barriers that actually make stations even more difficult to escape from in the event of a fire but on extra staff, equipment and trains. But investment on the scale that's needed will need Government sanction and that is the crunch.

It's all very well for Mrs Thatcher to turn up at a disaster with kind words but what really is needed is for the Prime Minister – for once – to put people before pounds. Otherwise the next disaster is just around the corner.

4 Piper Alpha

> We are faced with the frustration of keep having to say 'we told you so'. We don't want to do this – we want the situation changed before something happens.
>
> Roger Spiller, *Manufacturing, Science and Finance*

On 6 July 1988 the oil platform in the North Sea, Piper Alpha blew up with the loss of 167 lives, the world's worst oil disaster. Piper Alpha is different in a significant way from either Zeebrugge or King's Cross. It is a long time since it was considered a major hazard to cross the English Channel and those travelling on the *Herald of Free Enterprise* had every right to consider it was perfectly safe. Nor should it be considered a possibility that you might be burned to death on your way home from the office.

But drilling for oil in the North Sea is, by its very nature, hazardous – from the long (sometimes up to two-hour) helicopter flights to the platforms, to the actual nature of the substances being pumped out of the earth. It is obvious, because of this, that safety procedures should be as near foolproof as possible.

It was 9.31 p.m. on the evening of 6 July that the first blast occurred. It was severe enough to throw men out of their bunks. The men on Piper Alpha had been well trained – later many people were to say that had the training been different, more of them would have survived. As it was, they did what they had been told to do and remained in the accommodation block. There is now a good deal of criticism about the way British rigs are constructed, particularly with regard to the accommodation block.

Piper Alpha stood 500 feet out of the water and pumped out 167,000 barrels of oil and 23 million cubic feet of gas a day. The accommodation block was directly over the main drilling production area, a situation described by one of the survivors as 'a hotel sitting on a potential firebomb'. The reason was cost. It would cost a great deal more to provide a separate platform for workers although, as we shall see later, the Norwegian oil industry manages these things considerably better.

In the event the men in the accommodation block waited for nearly an hour to learn what they should do – and most of them died. They had been taught that the most likely method of evacuation would be by helicopter but the helicopter pad had been destroyed in the explosion. The control room was too severely damaged for messages to be passed through it to the men. While they sat there the fire engulfed the four-storey building and cut off all means of escape.

Eventually some of them decided to go and fought their way out through the flames only to find there were no boats either. They jumped straight into the sea, something they had been warned against doing.

'There was plenty of time', one survivor, Andrew Machan, was later to tell the *Observer* (10 July 1988).

'to put on survival suits. We must have been in that situation for more than an hour. People were going up and down the four levels of the accommodation block, trying doors to see if we could get out. We were surrounded – trapped from the word go.

There was no panic, but people were going off on their own – trying the west side, trying to calculate which way the wind was blowing. After about an hour, there was a series of explosions, some minor, some major, about twenty in all'.

I went to level B, where my office is. Someone shouted. 'There's a bit of fresh air here', and we opened the doors. *Tharos* (the fire-fighting ship) had come over and was spraying water and that gave us time to jump out. About half a dozen men followed me. The steelwork I was climbing down was red hot. I was dancing across. My hands were burned. I was in the water for about twenty minutes before being picked up.

The rescue operation was on a massive scale and the fact that there were survivors at all was due to the skill and bravery of the rescuers, but in spite of their efforts 167 men died.

The chairman of the owners of the platform, Dr Arnold Hammer of Occidental Petroleum, was visibly shaken when he arrived in Aberdeen and promised compensation to the employees and their families. But not many of those on the rig were direct employees of Occidental – most were working for contractors as is the normal practice in the North Sea.

The government immediately declared that there would be a full inquiry and its findings would be made public. (At the time of writing it is still continuing.) It also announced that the number of accidents in the North Sea had fallen between 1986 and 1987. But, as the *Observer* reported (10 July 1988) this gives a misleading picture. The number of serious accidents had actually jumped from 44 in 1984, to 85 in 1985 and 72 in 1986 before falling to 38 in 1987.

It did not take long for a great deal of hitherto unreported unease to bubble to the surface. The Piper Alpha platform was over twelve years old. There had been trouble with its stability when it was being built; and, according to a BBC *Newsnight* item on 12 August 1988, it had stood in the North Sea for several months before it had been painted with anti-corrosive paint. Oil ran from it along a 28" pipeline 128 miles long to the Flotta Terminal in Orkney, run by Occidental. Gas was piped 34 miles north through an 18" pipeline to join an Elf-operated pipeline running from the Frigg field to the natural gas terminal at St Fergus near Peterhead. It also sent gas down a pipeline to meet the power needs of the generating plant on the Occidental Claymore production platform and took gas from the Texaco Tartan field twelve miles away.

It was, therefore, an exceptionally complex piece of equipment. It weighed 34,000 tonnes. Its four legs were buried 150 feet into the sea-bed.

It soon transpired that the 1988 disaster had not been the first accident on the platform. In 1982 three oilmen died when they fell 70 feet from the platform's access gangway. More significantly, in view of what was to happen, there had been an earlier and extremely serious explosion on the rig in 1984. This had resulted in the evacuation of 75 men, 55 of whom had to be treated in hospital for minor injuries.

An internal Department of Energy inquiry was launched into this earlier incident and the results were never made public. The blast, apparently, occurred in a gas-processing module, shattering windows and doors in the accommodation area and bringing down the roof of the recreation room. It was followed by a fire which took an hour to extinguish and was confined to that area. There were 236 men on the platform at the time (a similar number to those on the platform at the time of the 1988 disaster), although it is actually designed to accommodate only 200.

The confidential report said the explosion happened in a processing area where natural gas liquids were separated from dry gas. Copies of the report were held both by the Department of Energy and Occidental Petroleum, and a list of 'action points' was sent to the oil company by safety officers from the department; but the inspector felt that prosecution was unnecessary, so the findings of the report were never made public.

A former Occidental safety manager, John Donaldson, was widely quoted as saying that many of the men who died in the 1988 explosion could have been saved if two important recommendations made in the confidential 1984 report had not been rejected. He told the *Observer* (10 July 1988) that the platform had had a long history of safety lapses and faced commercial pressure to operate at maximum output.

Mr Donaldson, who had retired in 1985, said, 'It is fair to say that Piper Alpha would be the most highly dangerous platform in the North Sea'. Occidental's management, he continued, was unfamiliar with the complexity of British safety regulatory bodies and the whole issue was, therefore, 'confused. Occidental plant was loaded to the point of being questionable about its "all-up" weight. The legs were strengthened to support the loading. But if you get such a major fire, the "all-up" weight causes imbalance, dropping the accommodation module into the sea.'

The rig's gas flare also created serious problems. 'It would flare back to the north face of the accommodation block and crack the surfaces of the lifeboats. Some of the lifeboats had to have water sprayed on them constantly to maintain them for use. The platform accommodated so many people that it was difficult for safety procedures to be fully enforced.'

The two recommendations in the confidential report that he felt should have been implemented were: that the wooden accommodation should have been replaced with less combustible material; and that steel blast walls should have been fitted next to the gas compression chamber, believed to have been the seat of the explosion.

Only thirty-seven of the men on board the rig at the time of the disaster were directly employed by Occidental. The rest were contract workers. Comments from a number of men were quoted in the BBC *Newsnight* programme on 12 August 1988. 'Vibration was enough to wake me up five or six times during the night', said one. 'There was so much movement on the platform I couldn't sleep', said another. 'Jokes were cracked about the movement in the canteen when coffee slopped about in the mugs . . . I wondered whether the vibration caused some kind of metal fatigue – it was an old platform with lots of extra gear on board. I thought it might be like an old car with too many people on board and then the suspension goes.'

Men spoke to the media anonymously for fear of losing their jobs with contractors. Others wrote to local papers asking that their names and addresses be withheld. A number said they would be too frightened to appear before an official inquiry in case they put their careers in jeopardy. One survivor, however, Andy Machan, was quoted in the media as alleging that alarms on Piper Alpha, as elsewhere, were sometimes deliberately by-passed.

> We've got a job to do and we get a spurious-type alarm and it's slowing up doing the job because the alarm's going off, so what we'd do is to get the electrician to pull the wires and disconnect the alarm until such time as we get the job done and then restore the alarm to its usual condition again.

Occidental admitted that certain safety systems were by-passed during some operations but that this was strictly controlled under a 'permit to work' system, which specified the safety procedures to be followed.

Survivors of the explosion spoke of a smell of gas which was particularly pungent that week. One worker was made so ill by it that he had to go to the medical officer with pains in the head and was told he was the fifth person to report that day. The gas, he thought, came from the gas compressor unit, the 'gas com'. The gas compressor had recently been shut down for difficult maintenance work.

A row over safety on the rig platform two years earlier had led to the worker-management safety committee being abandoned and it had not been reformed. Roger Spiller of the Manufacturing, Science and Finance Union (MSF), says that workers on Piper Alpha were not satisfied the management was taking their suggestions seriously and so had walked out. He believed that the oil companies were safety conscious but that there is no independent watchdog to check safety on platforms and rigs. There is no obligation for the oil companies to have a safety committee.

Piper Alpha threw up a whole range of questions about the way the industry is operated in general. Workers are supposed to have undergone a survival course before working on the rigs and have a certificate to prove it. But some contractors make the men pay for their own course – which can cost up to £300 – so there is something of a trade in forged certificates. A BBC reporter, in a news item transmitted just six weeks after the event, produced evidence of how he had picked up just such a blank Aberdeen Survival Centre certificate for the price of a few drinks. A more elaborate forgery, a properly printed safety card with photograph, cost £60.

Roger Spiller, who is the offshore organizer for the MSF, admits that this does go on but that it is not widespread. Contractors work to very tight financial limits, limits which are getting tighter all the time. Some make their employees pay for the survival course themselves and then repay the sum involved over a period of two years, which helps ensure that the trained employee remains with the contractor for that time. The MFU considers this to be acceptable but does not approve of the contractors who pay the fee for the men and then deduct it from their wages over the next two years.

Men who raised safety issues claimed that they were blacklisted by contractors competing in a cut-throat market. Matty O'Connor, a platform rigger and safety officer, said he was blacklisted because he raised too many safety issues and claims that contractors keep a record of such men, the key to which is their National Insurance number. When they call about a job they are asked first for their number, their past history is then checked out and they are refused the job.

Regarding Piper Alpha, it gradually began to emerge that the possible reason the disaster had happened on such a scale was because gas had continued to flow along a pipeline from Texaco's Tartan oilfield twelve miles away for an hour after the first explosion. Labour MP Frank Doran, in a letter to the Energy Secretary, Cecil Parkinson, asked:

> If my information is correct, the valves on this pipeline were not closed for at least an hour and ten minutes after the Mayday call and at least 40 minutes after the call to ships to move away from the platform. Is there no automatic system which should operate when the pipeline has ruptured? If there was an automatic system did it malfunction on July 6 and – if so – why?

At the time of writing that question remains unanswered.

On 30 September 1988 the results of the Department of Energy's initial technical investigations were published. Failure to record the absence of a pressure relief valve was pinpointed as a likely cause of the disaster. The missing valve in the gas compression module could have led to the release and subsequent ignition of a section of pipework. On the day of the disaster the vital valve had been removed after an injection pump was described as 'running rough'. Scaffolding had been erected to remove the large valve after an electrician obtained a permit for the work. He completed a test and calibration around 6 p.m., about three hours before the first explosion.

He was told that the crane needed to lift the valve back to the module would not be available until the next day so he returned the work permit to the control room where it was 'suspended'. He intended to reinstate the valve the following day. At the next shift hand-over there was no reference to the missing valve in the log control book, although the oncoming shift might have been briefed orally.

The initial report pointed to a series of safety failures on Piper Alpha. First, fire pumps, which had been switched to manual operation – apparently for the safety of divers working underwater who can be sucked into underwater pipes – could not start automatically. This is the so-called 'deluge' system whereby a platform is deluged in water automatically if there is a fire. As a result of their being switched off, there was no water to extinguish the fire.

Secondly, because the severity of the accident increased dramatically after the initial explosion – very probably caused by the continuing inflow of gas from the Texaco platform – mass evacuation proved impossible due to the total envelopment of the accommodation in dense black smoke and flame. It was impossible to take the men off by helicopter.

Thirdly, 1200 barrels of fuel were stored above the gas separation and compression modules and, fourthly, two inflatable life rafts which were launched failed to inflate.

The force of the initial explosion was such that it caused substantial damage to the main control room, electrical power generators, power distribution systems and the 'battery uninterruptible power' supply systems. All essential and emergency services were disabled almost instantaneously.

Roger Spiller considers that if a manual system was disconnected because of divers working underneath the rig in the water, then someone should have been standing by all the time to put the system back on to automatic. Clearly if the 'deluge' system had operated it would have had a substantial effect on the fire.

Also, although the men did exactly what they were trained to do and waited to be given instructions to evacuate in an orderly manner, the system now needs to take into account what they should do when instructions cannot be given because the control room itself is knocked out. Individual actions are not encouraged on oil platforms but in this case it was those who took matters into their own hands who survived, the rest did not.

The biggest single bone of contention, however, is that the Department of Energy is responsible both for the production and revenue from the rigs and also for health and safety matters. Inspectors regularly inspect the rigs but there are only seven of them to cope with several hundreds of rigs. They never arrive unannounced and, according to the MSF, whatever the government might say, their average stay on a rig is a day. What is needed, say workers, is for the safety checks to be carried out entirely independently and handed over to the Health and Safety Executive.

The response from the Department of Energy was that this was unnecessary. There was no conflict of interest in having production, revenue and safety all under the aegis of the same department.

Piper Alpha threw into sharp relief the difference between the way the Norwegians organize these things and the way we do. Not only are Norwegian rigs luxurious in their accommodation, they are designed so that accommodation is as far away from the production areas as possible. STATOIL, the Norwegian oil company, uses 'risk analysis' to avoid accidents. They estimate the risk to people on their rigs as three deaths in 10,000 years. There are seven blast walls between the living accommodation and the producing areas and the accommodation has, under it, free-fall lifeboats which can hit the sea in three seconds. The Norwegians have insisted that even their oldest platforms are brought up to the newest standards of safety and they were shocked by the magnitude of the Piper Alpha disaster.

Each of the Norwegian platforms has its own safety officer on board who has the right to shut down the whole operation if he thinks it necessary. Workers are represented on the platform safety committee.

Such care makes producing oil more expensive, up by about 10 per cent. A spokesman for STATOIL says that in the order of things people come first, followed by the design of the platforms, then their efficiency and last of all profit.

Norway's safety inspectors arrive unannounced, either in their own helicopters or, if on a routine flight, it is ensured that those on the platform do not know an inspector is aboard. Energy Secretary Cecil Parkinson, who has repeatedly expressed his satisfaction with the existing situation here, says rightly that in Norway too the inspectorate comes under the same department as that which sees to the production of the oil. What he does not say, however, is that the inspectors do not report to that department but to a separate ministry, the Department of Labour.

So the situation by 22 September 1988 was that the official inquiry was still going on (although initial technical findings had been published), that the Department of Energy and its minister were standing by their faith in the existing system and the unions and the men were pressing for an independent safety inspectorate. Surely, in view of all the activity since Piper Alpha, there could not be another accident so soon?

There could and there was. On 22 September a massive explosion rocked the Ocean Odyssey drilling rig and this was followed by a huge fire. Again there was an hour before evacuation began but sixty-six out of the sixty-seven men on board were safely taken off. The only man who died was a young radio operator, Tim Williams.

Once again there have been allegations that there was ample evidence of impending trouble. Vital hydraulic pipes controlling the system that might have stopped a blow out were known to be leaking at least a week before the drilling rig exploded, according to a report in the *Guardian* (26 September 1988). Two survivors, Nick Owen and Tony Church both employed by a sub-contractor, Sub-Sea Offshore, explained that hydraulic fluid was seen escaping from at least three tubes on both sides of the command lines that operated the safety system on the sea-bed, but the drilling rig was not halted, they said.

The leak had been spotted by a submersible camera and immediately reported to the operators of the rig. Written reports on the apparent damage were also given to Atlantic Richmond (ARCO), who own the drilling concession. The men had seen fluid leaking both from the main and standby systems. Mr Owen said:

> We called the engineer responsible in and he immediately called in his superior. His supervisor observed both of the leaks and was heard to say by both Tony and I that he intended to do nothing about the leaks. To repair the leaks the drilling operation would have to be suspended. The supervisor told the sub-sea engineer, 'We don't want to do that, do we?' He didn't expect an answer.

A written log detailing the leaks was sent to the ARCO representative on board but he made no request to view them. This was a week before the blow out. The two men also claimed that the standby motor on the hydraulic system on the rig which powers the blow out preventor was known to be burnt out and that another mechanical valve inside the blow out preventor had been damaged and was not working for two days immediately before the blow out.

Another issue was raised by Jim Murphy, a 'mud engineer' (an engineer in charge of adjusting the mud fluid used in drilling). He spoke extensively to the media about gas leaks. He told the *World at One* interviewer, on 23 September, that men had become physically ill with leaking gas and its effects. He said that leaks of 65 per cent were recorded on the drill floor and well over 100 per cent, off the scale, in other areas. 'You've got to say it was unsafe', he added.

He elaborated on this to the *Observer* (25 September 1988). He said the rig's operators, ARCO, had a copy of a telex which proved his claim that it had been warned of high levels of gas on the rig. He wrote the telex, describing gas levels of 'over 100% rising from the well hole', a couple of days before the explosion. The company denied this. Said Mr Murphy, 'the telex was one of many warnings they have had. They get morning reports from their own drilling supervisors, from me, from their own geologists, from Exlog (the exploration logging company which measures data from the well). They know there were unprecedented levels of gas on that rig for six weeks'. He said the company had not been able to drill for several days because of the problems and that the drill itself had to be pulled back from 16,160 feet to 12,000 feet. The well was so dangerous, he said, 'they should simply have put a plug on it'.

A week after the blow out, union officials called for an inquiry after Atlantic Richmond admitted it had been due to a mechanical failure. 'For six weeks it was known that there were defects in this well', said Mr Campbell Reid of the Inter-Union Offshore Committee. Atlantic Richmond said a fault in the complex underwater equipment was the most probable cause of the blow out and fire.

As with Piper Alpha, oil workers have been deeply concerned that they might lose their jobs if they speak out, although Energy Secretary Cecil Parkinson has kept emphasizing that they will not be victimized if they come forward. For a considerable while after this last accident, Mr Parkinson was adamant that the current safety procedures did not need to be changed and repeated his views volubly to the media. Again he said he saw no conflict of interest in the Department of Energy monitoring itself and he did not see the need for safety committees on rigs.

On 7 October 1988 he changed his mind on safety committees, saying that a consultative document will be sent to management and unions proposing the change which will remove the exemption for oil and gas companies under the Health and Safety Act, not to set up safety committees on offshore rigs. However he remained quite adamant that trade unions will not have a right to representation on these committees.

The change of heart came in a letter to Labour's shadow energy spokesman, John Prescott, MP, who welcomed the new safety committees but condemned the decision on union recognition. He pointed out that it was the first time that an attempt had been made to remove trade unions from health and safety work, something which is required by law in all other industries – and he also wondered if this will apply to the electricity and coal industries when they are privatized.

Both accidents raised large issues, the most important of which is how can workers who see that something is badly wrong ensure that action is taken? There are others, too. It appears that the fire-fighting ship, *Tharos*, which played such an important part in the Piper Alpha disaster, was to have been sold off as it was considered unnecessary. Why? The number of standby vessels in the southern sector of the North Sea, serving over sixty rigs, has been reduced by half as a cost-saving exercise. The oil companies say they can do this as the original number of ships was in excess of official regulations. The MSF argues that if it was felt that keeping the ships on standby, at a cost of £1000 a day, was necessary before, then why isn't it now?

As to safety and maintenance, this has been cut back by around 50 per cent at a time when platforms are ageing and needing more attention, especially with regard to corrosion. The oil companies say that the cutbacks have not affected safety as equipment is now so much more sophisticated that it does not require the amount of maintenance and checking that it used to. Is this really the case? And can we be sure that what is said officially is correct, if there is no independent inspectorate and only seven inspectors in all?

Of Piper Alpha, Allan Millar of the Professional Divers' Association said: 'That rig had quite a reputation. It was felt that if anything did happen it would be on that particular platform.'

Of Ocean Odyssey, Jim Murphy said: 'They should have abandoned that rig long before'.

The fiancée of Piper Alpha victim, Craig Barclay, said: 'It's important. We've got to find out what happened. So many lives were lost that shouldn't have been. People have got to come forward and speak up for the men who died.'

The MSF's assistant general secretary, Roger Lyons, said: 'It's tragic that only on the basis of coffins brought ashore can we get improvements in safety in the North Sea'; and Roger Spiller of the same union added: 'We are faced with the frustration of keep having to say "we told you so". We don't want to do this – we want the situation changed *before* something happens.'

5   Air Traffic Control and Pilot Fatigue

> We seem to have embarked on a programme of learning by
> catastrophe.
>
> Bill Brett, *assistant general secretary of the*
> *Institution of Professional Civil Servants*

Air Traffic Control

If you ask people who think about these things to speculate on
what they think the next disaster will be, then nine times out of
ten they come up with 'a mid-air collision in British airspace'. It
is quite clear that whatever reassurances may be given by
government or the Civil Aviation Authority (CAA), people are
just not happy. They know the airways are desperately congested
– the summer of 1988 was marked by people waiting not just
hours but days for flights out of British airports; they also feel
that they are not being told the true situation. Being told that the
number of 'near misses' is decreasing has more of the ring of
statistical truth about it than the real thing.

The responsibility for airspace policy is vested in the National
Air Traffic Services (NATS), which is responsible both to the
Civil Aviation Authority and the Ministry of Defence, and is
invariably and exclusively held by a serving officer in HM forces.
Air Traffic Control, as the evidence given by the Institution of
Professional Civil Servants (IPCS) to the House of Commons
Select Committee into Air Traffic Control Safety pointed out:

> exists to provide a safe, orderly and expeditious (i.e. economic),
> flow of air traffic . . . Air Traffic Controllers (ATCOs) determine
> the time at which aircraft start their engines, begin to taxi, the

route to the runway, the runway in use, the time of takeoff, the climb profile, the route in the air, the altitude of the flight, often the speed of the flight, the descent profile, holding requirements and the approach sequence and approach path.

The London Air Traffic Control Centre alone handles more than one million flights per annum. On average each aircraft has 200 seats and is controlled for 30 minutes.

The IPCS noted grimly:

While safety is paramount, the growth in air traffic movements and the pressure on current airline economics produces ever increasing demands for expedition. *This conflict between safety and expedition has brought the system to breaking point.*

The IPCS began pressing for something to be done – and quickly – back in February 1986 when it became quite apparent that traffic levels were increasing beyond the level the Air Traffic Controllers considered safe. 'We could see the CAA doing nothing', said the assistant general secretary, Bill Brett,

except for providing the infra-structure, and all against a background of the government talking about 'liberalisation'. When we tried to put our case we were told it had nothing to do with us, that matters such as liberalisation of the air lines was not appropriate for discussion with the unions representing ATC staff. But when we looked at just one of the routes, between this country and Holland, we could see that air traffic on that alone would increase the number of flights per day by 39%.

As the evidence to the Commons Select Committee pointed out, it was not just the sheer increase in traffic which was the problem – it was also the different *mix* of traffic. Air Traffic Control would be relatively easy if all the traffic was of the same size and moved at the same speed. But liberalization has, and will, lead to small start-up airlines with cheap and cheerful slow-moving aircraft, so not only will there be an increase in traffic but the different mix will make it harder to control.

Throughout 1987 the CAA responded to any criticism or expressed fear with the response, 'we can handle it'. Yet it became manifestly obvious, particularly during the summer of 1988, that this they could not do, as delay stacked on delay in our overcrowded skies. The CAA has told the Select Committee that it does not foresee air traffic growing at a rate which is not manageable – the unions disagree.

The flight paths for aircraft are rather like motorways in the sky. If you try and mix too many kinds of aircraft out of Gatwick, smaller and slower planes from the new deregularized air companies vying with the big 757s, 767s and suchlike, then, in Bill Brett's words: 'it's like putting milk floats on the M1'. You have two choices, either to slow everything down to let them in and then the whole system jams up, or take a risk – and, say the Air Traffic Controllers, 'We can't take risks'.

The upshot of all the openly expressed concern was that in 1987 Flow Traffic Controls were introduced which act, quite simply, as traffic lights in the sky. For the Air Traffic Controller, it means he has to keep the plane on the ground until he knows there's a space for it right through its journey until it lands at its destination. That, they say, is going to have a bigger and bigger impact between now and 1995 but there's no other way of dealing with the problem. In its evidence the CAA said that by 1992, when full liberalization comes in, 'centralized control function' will be in use, that is specified air corridors which will increase the capacity of the system by 30 per cent – but all forecasts show that traffic will also have increased by 30 per cent by that time.

'We have a computer at West Drayton', said Brett, 'which should be in the Science Museum.' (It 'went down' on a number of occasions during the summer of 1988.) It is an IBM 1920 model built in 1966 from a design first produced in the early 1960s. It is one of the last ones still in use anywhere in the world. He continued:

It is unreliable now because it is a computer of the Stone Age. Its other problem is that its software is 'rusty'. It's using sixteen-year-old software which has been patched and patched. We have a new computer coming in which is an IBM 3081 HOLST from the USA to replace it but we spent so long not getting things right that we have ended up with no option but to buy American and have, therefore, bought ourselves a computer which is not compatible with any of the other European computers used for the same purpose!

In August 1988 the newspapers were full of horror stories about problems in the air. A report in the *Daily Telegraph* on 11 August 1988 noted that pilots are becoming increasingly worried about safety and fear that something awful might happen unless action is taken quickly to relieve congestion at airports and in the air. The closure of the Gatwick runway brought together pilots' three worst nightmares, as identified by Dr Ian Perry, a leading consultant in aviation medicine.

He told the newspaper that they were frightened by airport safety standards, especially at Gatwick; delays resulting in the chance of running out of fuel while waiting to land; and dangerous pilot fatigue (a topic which will be dealt with in depth later).

On 10 August at Gatwick, for the second time in a week, the main runway failed to open at 6 a.m. after nightly resurfacing work, causing the early morning wave of arriving aircraft to 'stack' in holding patterns at between 14,000ft and 23,000ft over the Channel. Some were forced to land elsewhere. One pilot, told he could only use the emergency runway at Gatwick, refused to land and circled until the main one opened. Holes in the main runway had been found during the pre-opening inspection after resurfacing work.

Coping with all this, at the end of the line, are the Air Traffic Controllers. It is not a job, according to Bill Brett, which requires inspiration. The worst that can happen to people in most jobs is that they might miss something. ATCs can't do that – they have to be on the ball all the time. It's an odd kind of person who makes a good controller. 'He or she needs maths, physics and discipline – you can forget about imagination! You don't want an imaginative controller who'll find a new way of doing it. You need someone who can look at thirty options and take the best one – in thirty seconds . . . ' It takes four years to train one and even though the intake of trainees has been upped from forty to eighty a year (after the CAA had announced at one time that it was seeking some 10 per cent redundancies), there are still not enough of them. About 50 per cent of those accepted for training do not make it through the three-year apprenticeship course.

This is aggravated by the career system, as an Air Traffic Controller who has worked efficiently and well at, say, Cardiff airport would have to retrain for six months before working at Heathrow. The union also wants to see a legalized limit on the number of hours an Air Traffic Controller can work. As Brett said: 'Pilots are limited, even lorry drivers are limited, but Air Traffic controllers are not. Yet there are few other jobs where it is so necessary to remain alert.'

In our overcrowded skies the possibility of a mid-air collision is a very real one in spite of the soothing statistics which appear to show that 'near misses' in the air are actually declining. The reason the CAA can say this is because they only count the air misses which are reported to them by pilots, not those clearly seen by the Air Traffic Controllers on their screens.

The chance of two pilots actually seeing each other at 3,000 feet in cloud is, say the experts, pretty remote and largely a matter of luck. Yet the controllers have in front of them radar screens with 'blips' on them, one for each aircraft, and they can see at a glance when aircraft get too close to each other. But if a controller reports it to the Civil Aviation Authority, however great the detail he can provide, it is not counted in their statistics as a 'near miss'!

The parallel, said Bill Brett, would be to say that if you see your car being stolen, then that's theft, 'but if I see your car being stolen and tell you, then it isn't! It's as stupid as that.'

Apart from the obvious reason why reports from Air Traffic Controllers should be accepted if they are properly backed up, there is another. Pilots are only human and, like all members of a similar profession, they tend to hang together and would not willingly want to 'shop' a fellow pilot even if they did know he had been involved in such an incident.

Well into the summer of 1988 the CAA was still giving comforting news about near misses, yet within a matter of weeks there were two which spelled out the truth of the situation.

The first, on 9 June, involved a Concorde which, according to a report acquired by the *Mail on Sunday*, showed that the supersonic aircraft was only ten seconds from disaster and that the near miss, which had involved a Tristar jet, had taken place directly above thousands of homes near to Heathrow. The *Mail* accused the Civil Aviation Authority of 'hushing it up'. The incident was not reported to Transport Secretary Paul Channon, despite a personal pledge from the CAA's chairman, Christopher Tugendhat, that the minister was to be told of every incident.

A total of 198 passengers were aboard the two aircraft and even when Air Traffic Control realized there was something badly wrong, there was still a problem as the aircraft used different radio frequencies so they had to be contacted separately.

Hard on the heels of this piece of information came another – that a helicopter of the Queen's Flight, carrying Princess Margaret, came within a few hundred feet of a fully loaded British Airways jumbo jet as it took off from Heathrow and turned into the same flight path. Again the incident was not reported as a near miss even though the Air Traffic Controller involved immediately notified the CAA that he believed the aircraft had been only 300 feet from each other. The Ministry of Defence said later that the pilot of the helicopter was fully aware of the situation but there is no proof that the pilot of the jumbo jet was.

The Civil Aviation Authority played down both incidents but it is worrying that these two only came out into the open because, in the first case, one of the aircraft involved was Concorde and, in the second, a member of the Royal Family was on board.

Air Traffic Controllers estimate that there are at least 50 per cent more near misses than the CAA is prepared to admit. As Bill Brett said: 'You see there is no "average" over here for mid-air collisions because we've never had a civil one yet in UK airspace but they have had three in the USA in the last two years.'

Europe's airways are also hagridden with bureaucracy and it does seem remarkable that in so relatively small an area there is no standardized or centralized Air Traffic Control system – nor would Britain be likely to join if there was, given the present administration's attitude to everything European. Different countries have different training methods, different computers, different standards – and all set against the background of increasing air traffic.

There are other local problems too. Since the privatization of the British Airports Authority each airport has had to be run as a private company and, as is the case with all private companies, its first priority is to make a profit. Some, like Heathrow and Gatwick, very obviously do. Others like Prestwick in Scotland do not, while others, such as Edinburgh and Glasgow, are only marginally profitable. So the British Airports Authority is trying to take over air traffic control in Scotland from the Civil Aviation Authority and run it themselves.

Before privatization, all British Airports Authority airports had – by law – to use the Air Traffic Controllers at West Drayton but that legal safeguard went overboard with privatization. If they now want to use their own they can and, to try and ensure greater profitability, they could theoretically use fewer controllers working longer hours in a job where, as we have seen, the stress factor does not lend itself to long shifts.

Finally there is the real joker in the pack. At present if you decide you want to start up an airline flying, say, from Luton to Malaga, then you have to get the permission of both governments and this is quite a lengthy and exhaustive business. In 1993 all that will go out of the window because, from 1 January 1993, unless both governments say they will not agree to it, the route will then be automatically allowed under the new de-regulation system.

Then there will be, as the IPCS put it, 'an explosion of Mickey Mouse airlines flying out of third-level airports into other third-level airports, cutting out all the big ones, resulting in an increase in traffic of between twenty and thirty per cent in one year'.

The immediate response of the government to all this concern – over the ageing West Drayton computer, the overcrowded runways, the growing congestion and the coming explosion of liberalization – was summed up in a gung-ho press release issued by Lord Brabazon, Minister for Aviation and Shipping, on 30 August 1988. He said:

The UK government sees no reason to abandon its free market policies in the face of air traffic congestion. We are determined to find ways of reconciling our free market policies with the limits imposed upon us by infrastructure constraints. We shall strive to remove these constraints as quickly as possible. The twin policies of liberalisation and privatisation have helped the UK build up a competitive and adaptable air industry.

He continued in the same remarkable vein.

The market, if given its head, will be far more adept than the heavy-handed regulator at finding ways of avoiding bottlenecks and in making the best use of the scarce infrastructure available ... The darkest cloud on the horizon of the industry is not congestion. It is the risk that governments will respond to the problem of congestion by retreating into excessive regulation of the industry. That is not an approach this government wishes to adopt.

No, indeed. By the autumn of 1988 aware of mounting criticism, especially from the public, both the government and the CAA announced what appeared to be new measures to improve the situation but, on close examination, this does not prove to be the case. There would be a new computer at West Drayton; we already knew that and it was not pointed out that the new computer is not, itself, the best buy – although it can only be an improvement on the creaking machine presently in use. Also, there would be 'flow management' which would improve the movement of aircraft; but, as we have seen, flow management is subject to many constraints, not least slower old aircraft and fast modern ones sharing the same airspace.

The Institution of Professional Civil Servants wants to see far more investment in new technology although it is doubtful that even if that were to be put in hand today, it would be up and running by the time de-regularization comes in in 1992. The Air Traffic Controllers consider that the only safe way is to 'cap' the number of aircraft that are allowed to operate in our skies, but that runs directly counter to the government's arguments for de-regulation and letting market forces rip.

The IPCS points out that however attractive the idea of free-for-all airlines might be to some, experience in the USA suggests that such freedom and price cutting lasts only as long as it takes for most of the small airlines to be swallowed up by the larger ones. It also leads to inefficiency, and it is now said cynically that when an American airline pilot lands his aircraft on time they give him a standing ovation as the event is so rare.

We can allow, theoretically, an unlimited number of airlines to operate in de-regulated skies; but not unlimited, nor expanding, are the amount of runways we have, the number of Air Traffic Controllers employed and – most importantly – the amount of airspace we have.

When the chips are down, said Bill Brett, 'our members are also aware, following the Zeebrugge disaster, that it is the licensed personnel rather than the policy-making senior management who find themselves in the dock and held responsible following such an event'.

There are two views as to what is likely to happen. To quote Lord Brabazon, 'we will maintain our free market approach because we believe the flexibility and responsiveness of the market holds many of the answers'.

And as Bill Brett said: 'We seem to have embarked on a programme of learning by catastrophe. The risks of a mid-air collision over central London are now so great that it is not a question, in my view, of *if* such a collision will happen; it's a question of *when* . . . '

Pilot Fatigue

In 1973 the British Air Line Pilots' Association (BALPA) produced a report on *Flight Fatigue*. It was immediately withdrawn and suppressed after publication, allegedly on the grounds that some remarks in it were libellous, although it is hard to see – reading one of the rare existing copies – how this could be.

One might assume, some fifteen years on, that whatever the report contained must be highly irrelevant by now. But, as shall be shown, not only is this not the case but the situation has even worsened as the number of flights has increased. In fact the crucial findings of this suppressed report are as relevant now as ever they were.

It opened with the chilling statement:

The Association believes that Pilot Fatigue has now become the major current threat to air safety. Unless very significant changes are made to the Legislation and Guidelines, Pilots will not be able to fulfil the requirements of their Licences in ensuring the safety of their passengers ... This critical point has been reached because the Authorities, the Operators and the Industry have been treating the pilot as if he were another piece of computerised equipment.

These words came in the foreword signed by Captain E. S. Linstead, then chairman of BALPA.

It continued:

The greatest problem of all, his exposure to dehumanised work patterns, has received the least attention. The Pilot is the most vital component in the aircraft control loop yet he is the component whose limitations and vulnerability are the least considered ...

One wonders why, if a few remarks were considered libellous, the only comprehensive investigation undertaken by any recognized aviation authority at that time was not re-published with the supposed libels removed. The most obvious answer is not a reassuring one. The committee which undertook the survey and reported could hardly be said to have lacked experience – it consisted of two captains and four first officers who between them had some 70,000 hours of civil and military flying, four university graduates and a member of the Air Safety Group, a body established by Parliament to protect the interests of the travelling public.

As Second Flight Officer Wright 747 BA wrote to his trade paper, *The Log*, after the report was suppressed:

As co-author of the Flight Fatigue Report, I had to suffer its repression and eventual burning. As Chairman of the Medical Group, for years I was promoting the cause of members, hence treading on the toes of the status quo ... and a few years ago I was sacked – the fate of those who rock the BALPA boat.

The majority of aviation accidents (some 80–85 per cent) can be assigned broadly to 'pilot error' and the remainder to mechanical malfunctions, so how did it ever arise that pilots accepted a rostering system which could lead to critical levels of fatigue? Experienced pilots say it is because those involved in east-west-east flights spend most of their lives in a state of limbo, permanently suffering jet lag. The answer lies right back in the early days of commercial flying.

Before the Second World War commercial aviation hardly existed and it was during the war that the rapid strides were made which were the basis for modern airline flying. The learning cycle, with piston-engined machines, was very short and by 1959 these had given way to jet propulsion. During the brief twelve-year period of the slower machines, pilots could generally work on long-distance flights for up to twenty-four hours of duty. Both operators and pilots treated the new airline industry as an extension of wartime flying operations when long hours were endured and sleep taken when and where possible.

The first official recognition of the dangers of 'Pilot Fatigue' was the report of an inquiry into a crash at Singapore in 1954 with heavy loss of life. It was discovered that the pilot had been on duty for about twenty-four hours and crashed his machine in clear daylight when landing. The inquiry stated he was probably suffering from an insidious type of fatigue of which he was unaware. Regulations followed but as little was known about the completely new type of activity on the system – repetitive loss of a whole night's sleep and multiple body-clock changes – officialdom did little to remedy the problem and sixteen-hour duties, often commencing late at night were – and still are – permitted.

Jet flying meant man challenged the environment in a completely new way, continually crossing the world at speeds never before experienced where each landing threw sleep and body functions into confusion. As the jet was twice as fast as the old airliners it replaced, it meant the pilot could do twice as much work in the same time and thus real profits from aviation were now assured.

Once the big jets came into operation then it was discovered that in an aircraft like a Boeing 707, which could carry three times the number of people in half the time of the older planes, only two pilots were needed to do the work of twelve. A piston-engined aircraft crew managed five return Atlantic crossings in a working month and this could now be doubled. The vital component in this revolution was the pilot, whose physical and mental condition was entrusted with the safety of the operation and to whom no thought was given.

Consequently the accident rate became phenomenal. According to Captain Arne Leibling, the world's leading authority, writing in *The Log* back in June 1966, the result was 'one fatal accident per week, one major incident every three and a half days . . . '. Crews experienced near double the fatigue with twice the time-zones, twice the time-loss and half of all flights being at night. The only way to alleviate the increased stress engendered by the new demands would be to increase the number of crews to match the situation – but this would have meant up-pricing the cost of travel to an unthinkable level.

All this, and other information contained in the suppressed BALPA report was brought to the attention of the aviation authorities but nothing was undertaken which might have helped prevent future loss of life, although a number of accidents have since been acknowledged as having been caused by fatigue-induced pilot error. However, as some 80 per cent of all accidents are in any event attributed to pilot error, then it is also easy not to take any deeper look into the possible underlying cause of that error.

It is also a useful get-out. If it could be proved that an accident was caused by pilot error then, according to law, there is no negligence on the part of government or operators and so only relatively small sums were forthcoming for the dead passengers' relatives – thus ensuring cheap aviation, low fares and no culpability. This is even more important now that, in this country, British Airways has been privatized. Aviation was also left outside the normal industrial regulations which control employees' fatigue, such as the EEC requirements concerning long-distance coach and truck drivers. Although governments are responsible in law for ensuring that fatigued pilots do not endanger their aircraft or passengers, this statutory duty was delegated to airline operators who were, on paper, obliged to compile crew rosters which did not cause fatigue. The system obviously is open to abuse with airline doctors being allowed no involvement in rostering and pilots putting their employment at risk if they complained.

When an accident happened, more often than not, the pilot would not be around to add his account of events and, even if he did survive, he was unlikely to plead fatigue as he would thereby inculpate himself.

Captain D. H. Wyles, an ex-British Airways BALPA pilot, made a study of such accidents after leaving British Airways, where he had become a thorn in their flesh. He began his career in the RAF, followed it by twenty-five years with British Airways (the final seven as a 747 captain) during which he was safety representative for all British Airways Longhaul Pilots. He made much use of information made available in the United States, where it is possible to get hold of it by using the Freedom of Information Act.

It was there that the full story of one of the world's worst aircraft disasters was fully investigated and documented – when a Pan Am B747 and a KLM B747 collided on a fog-bound runway at Tenerife in 1977 and 583 people were incinerated in their seats. The inquiry concluded the cause was one of Pilot Error and blamed the KLM captain for taking off without clearance to do so.

What Captain Wyles discovered in the United States was that the Pan Am crew had not slept properly for up to twenty-nine hours before. The 'Human Factor Report', carried out by the American Airways Pilots' Association, showed that the captain had '. . . had a nap the afternoon or evening prior to the flight . . . he reported at the airport about 00.45 local (0545 GMT). The accident occurred at 1706 GMT, 11 hours and twenty-one minutes later.

'The scheduled take-off in New York was 01.45 local, but because of late arrival of the aircraft from its origin in Los Angeles, the actual take-off was an hour late, 02.45 local'. If the captain was a normal human being, then, with normal sleep demands, he would have awoken in New York, the report estimates, at about 8 a.m., gone through that day having the 'nap' in the afternoon or evening and then started work at 1.45 a.m. the next day. Which means that at the time of the crash he had had twenty-nine hours without a proper sleep. It was not revealed what rest the other two officers had had in the previous twenty-four hours.

Had all this information been made freely available it might well have affected the outcome of the compensation settlements as it could have been argued that there was a dereliction of duty on the part of the airline companies involved.

So how do pilots feel now, fifteen years on from the suppressed BALPA report and eleven years after the accident at Tenerife?

First let us return briefly to the front page story in the *Daily Telegraph*, quoted in the section on Air Traffic Control, with its headline 'Pilot Fatigue and Congestion Will Cause Disaster'. Dr Ian Perry, the aviation medical expert, said: 'Everyone is worrying, and it seems only a matter of time before a very tired pilot and a very tired controller set in motion a train of events which could lead to a major disaster . . . ' He remained, he said, very concerned about pilot fatigue. During the summer of 1988 many of the crews landing at Gatwick in the early morning were extremely tired after flying two or three nights in succession with poor rest periods between.

'Something has got to be done about the rostering system to protect pilots from fatigue', he told the *Telegraph*.

Back in November 1987 the Civil Aviation Authority had said they would be cracking down on operators who disregarded the flight-time limitations, introduced in 1975 after the entire crew of an airliner fell asleep on the flight deck. But the CAA told the *Telegraph*, when Dr Perry's statement was put to them: 'Our inspectors have had very few fatigue complaints during the busy period this summer, but they have been keeping a much tighter watch on pilot hours.'

If pilots have really not been complaining to the CAA's inspectors, they have certainly been complaining anonymously through the pages of a quarterly publication called *Feedback*, which calls itself the 'Confidential Human Factors Incident Reporting Programme', or 'CHIRP' as it is popularly known. Those who publish CHIRP have every detail of the pilots who write in but they are promised total anonymity for their material – for obvious reasons as their jobs might well be at risk.

Here are just a few from the spring and summer of 1988. The first is from a pilot who left the airport three hours late on a seven-hour flight. 'Around 50W, Flight Engineer asleep – hasn't managed any sleep prior to afternoon pick-up. Around 40W, Co-Pilot asked if he could close his eyes. Engineer now awake. About half an hour later I dozed off momentarily when the Co-Pilot awoke, and then slept for one hour . . . at one stage really only the Engineer was fully awake. How could we have managed safely with a two-man crew?'

Next – 'three nights of this (there's one series in my log book of five in a row) doesn't do much for one's alertness'. This pilot then details a simple error he made which could have led to disaster. 'The problem was that I knew I was tired so I was being careful but realised all along that I was slow to make decisions, slow to recognise the situations developing and in the end made a simple error misreading an altimeter which nearly killed me. I suspect that it was not tiredness but real fatigue which caused the problem.'

And another – 'on the return leg at about 1600 I was awoken from a "cat-nap" by the co-pilot asking me if I was awake. Fortunately the aircraft has both height and heading holds and also, we were both very aware of being very tired . . . even cold air failed to alleviate the tiredness though and I finally deselected the "holds" and flew manually to keep myself awake.'

Others say, 'I would like to see more investigation into fatigue in the area of night flights . . . I find that on more than one occasion I have been so tired that I have changed frequency and either forgot to check in or checked in and then not replied to Air Traffic Control's response.' 'I have found the reports (in CHIRP) interesting, particularly those relating to fatigue on night sectors. This I believe to be the single most corrosive factor in relation to flight safety.' 'This summer I have become progressively more fatigued and I find that the time off is insufficient to "recharge" the system. Combine fatigue with inherently dangerous approaches such as Corfu at night and you have a deadly cocktail.'

The last pilot states that for the first time in twenty-four years of flying he has had to resort to taking sleeping pills in order to get some sleep before the next night flight. Noting that his letter to CHIRP marks 'the first time in my career that I have put pen to paper on such a matter', he pleads for something to be done.

'The odd long duty period is of little consequence. It is the combination of many such periods allied to near minimum rest periods (often involving trying to sleep during the day) that induces an insidious and deep tiredness.' He then goes on to make a point about CAP371, the official document which currently details the number of hours pilots can work in this country.

1 CAP371 is a monstrous document. The duty periods we are allowed to work are simply ridiculous when considered in conjunction with the minimum rest regulations.
2 Captain's discretion should only be used away from base to counteract exceptional circumstances e.g. Air Traffic Control Delays, technical delays. At the moment the use of discretion is becoming almost normal routine.
3 Taxi journeys after a flight [that is when the aircraft is taxying along the runway] should be included in the Flying Duty period.

It would have been possible to fill this whole book, let alone a chapter, with such concerns from pilots. I will end with these last two:

There is no doubt that commercial pressures on companies are forcing them to work to the maximum. One major company has put it quite openly to its pilots thus: 'To remain commercially viable within the industry we must be in as competitive a position as possible, especially in terms of crew ratios. All our competitors are, or very soon will be, working to CAP371 limitations. It therefore follows that this company needs to move to 371 limits.'

Lastly a pilot writing of this last summer, at Gatwick:

slot times to be airborne with a one minute tolerance, if missed then a five hour delay . . . crews operating on minimum rest as norm and extending hours to the maximum allowed. Runway closed at night for repairs result in diversions and then a repetition of the above . . . At the same time the Civil Aviation Authority says that there is nothing wrong with West Drayton

Air Traffic Control. British Airports' spokesman states only twenty out of 390 aircraft were delayed during the weekend of 11/12 June (1988) Who is trying to fool whom?

Surely there is someone 'out there' who knows that a continuation of the above is a *recipe for disaster*? If he *is* there he is welcome to sample some of the frustrations from my flight deck. I would suggest Saturdays at 0800 or early Sunday afternoon. Or shall we continue until the inevitable happens? Never mind – it's bound to be 'pilot error'.

There is absolutely no doubt whatsoever that pilot fatigue is not only a very real problem, it is also a well-documented problem about which there have been many warnings. Suppressing reports will not make that problem go away.

Now it has to be set against the background of the ageing and dilapidated computer at West Drayton (even if that is to be replaced within the next few years), over-stressed Air Traffic Controllers and the physical problems pilots are now experiencing at major airports, such as the continual running repairs to the Gatwick runway which makes it either difficult, or sometimes impossible, for incoming aircraft to land on it.

With regard to the Gatwick runway one of the most dramatic reports to come in during the summer of 1988 was that of a tired pilot who was diverted from Gatwick to Manchester Ringway and nearly landed on the M56 in mistake for the airport – but there were numerous other examples.

There was the Cathay Pacific 251 inbound from Hong Kong which found itself put back an hour in the queue at Gatwick with only ten minutes of fuel left and so had to divert without warning to Heathrow (*The Sunday Times*, 28 August 1988). There was the pilot of a BAE111 who, confused by the lighting of the three parallel strips at Gatwick mistakenly landed on the taxiway close to the emergency runway and nearly collided with another aircraft and yet another pilot who had also mistaken the taxiway for the emergency runway.

A report on that incident, which came into the possession of the *Daily Telegraph*, said it was not the fault of the captains, it was the fault of 'a lot of people saying everything was fine and dandy'. Yet another incident in the same report noted the comments of an Air Traffic Controller at Gatwick who said they were far from happy about the simultaneous use of the emergency runway and taxiway but that because of the sheer amount of traffic at the airport, management had said they had little choice. This report commented: 'Obviously financial considerations take priority over the safety of the public'.

Looming over all this now is total de-regulation in 1992 – more and more airlines, many operating on a shoestring; an even greater 'mix' of aircraft in the air at any one time; pilots pushed to the limit to ensure profitability; and out of date or, at best, incompatible equipment.

Of all the 'accidents waiting to happen' an air disaster caused either by problems with Air Traffic Control or pilot fatigue, or a mixture of both, seems – on available evidence - to be the most likely.

The subject is so important that perhaps this chapter should finish by repeating again the words spoken by Lord Brabazon, the minister responsible for what happens now and after deregulation for, if such a disaster occurs, he should be held accountable for them.

The darkest cloud on the horizon of the industry is not congestion. It is the risk that governments will respond to the problem of congestion by retreating into excessive regulation of the industry. That is not an approach this goverment wishes to adopt.

6   At Sea – Dropping the Pilot and Ro-Ro Ferries

... a recipe for disaster.

A. J. F. Foot, *Trinity House pilot*

Dropping the Pilot

October 1988 saw the end of a very old tradition indeed – the demise of the Trinity House pilot. In 1512 Henry VIII issued a charter to form a select group of men to serve as pilots. They were chosen from the volunteers who ran the Trinity Houses for distressed seamen, under the auspices of Holy Trinity Church, Deptford. This was the origin of what was one of the finest pilotage services in the world.

However, in order to save some £33m a year, the government decreed that from 1 October 1988 each port would be responsible for its own pilots within the limits of the district it covers. With regard to London that means the limit will now be the North Foreland and no longer a group of pilots based in Folkestone. As ex-Trinity House pilot, Mr A. J. F. Foot said in a letter to the *Daily Telegraph* on 11 August 1988: 'Instead each ship will be obliged to make its own way across the busy south-west traffic lane off the Kent coast to a rendez-vous at North Foreland.'

The seas of the English Channel are very shallow, the greatest depth of the Thames at 'springs' (the highest tides) is about 48 feet. As Mr Foot told the writer: 'We have to bring in ships up the river which draw all of 45 feet. We have to do this on a rising tide or they would obviously be stranded'. The pilot takes these large ships with the large draughts up the narrow channels as the tide rises until they are berthed in their 'berth boxes', where the river is especially deepened and not dependent upon the tides. There are many shallows and many shoals.

At first, as the Channel begins to narrow past Southampton, 'suggested routes' for shipping are shown on mariners' charts. But, as it narrows further, the sea-lanes narrow with it until the entire shipping land is only about three miles across. It then becomes the equivalent of a motorway with ships going up in one lane and down in the other. Ships are told that they cannot cross these fixed up and down routes – except for the larger vessels going into the Thames which have, until recently, been carefully taken across by Trinity House pilots.

Those ships that do have to cross, have to do so before they reach the 'Greenwich' buoy. There has also been, up to now, another route for smaller vessels known as 'the Downs'. The Downs route runs between the Goodwin Sands and the coastline and can be very tricky but is safe with a pilot. Because there will no longer be any Trinity House pilots stationed at Folkestone this route will no longer be allowed because, as well as the hazards of the Goodwins, it crosses the approaches to Dover, the busiest port in the world. So *all* vessels wanting to enter the Thames will now have to cross the major Channel shipping lanes.

As the Channel shipping lanes at this point are the busiest and most congested in the world, this will be rather like letting motor vehicles cross at random the M1 or M25 . . . and without a pilot too.

Trinity House pilots were second to none. Twenty years ago there were two hundred applicants for every job so, as Mr Foot said,

'your chances were 200 to 1 against being selected. You had to have had eight years as watchkeeper of a ship and obviously you have to have a deep sea Master's ticket. That was the first hurdle to cross. The other was age. If you reached the age of thirty-five and were still on the waiting list, they crossed you off. When you joined you spent two years as a fourth-class pilot piloting ships up to 1200 gross registered tonnage (GRT); one year as third-class piloting ships up to 4,500 GRT and one year as a second-class piloting ships up to 12,000. Thereafter you were first-class and dealt with ships of unlimited tonnage.

Our predecessors were remarkable men. They had to rely far more on instinct. Even fifty years ago instruments were very limited. There was no radar in fog, there were no echo sounders – they used a deep sea lead. Compasses could be inaccurate and compass error was not unusual. If the fog was dense then there was nothing for it but to anchor the ship.

When there is fog in the Channel you can't go on estimates. One mistake is enough. But the old pilots had a real feeling for the conditions. They were not enclosed in a bridge as we are nowadays with banks of instruments'.

The new regime started in October 1988 at the time the nights draw in and the weather deteriorates. It is the season for fog in the Channel. Since the Port of London Authority pilotage now ends at the North Foreland this means pilots are put on and taken off at Ramsgate, yet in the winter an easterly wind can blow for up to a fortnight and when this happens there is no way a pilot can be put on from Ramsgate. As there will be no pilotage out of Folkestone where this would be possible, the new port authority says ships will either have to stay outside or do the best they can. From now on there is a no man's land where pilotage is concerned, an area full of shoals and sandbanks where, if a ship's master gets it wrong, a ship could end up on shore and be broken up there, go aground on a shoal or become involved in a collision.

To quote Mr Foot again: 'This southern end of the North Sea can provide the meanest combination of circumstances ever to confront a mariner: shallow water, strong tides, dense fog and a massive concentration of shipping.'

So ships which have, hitherto, had to have pilots aboard, are now allowed on their own, up the Thames and across the shipping lanes. All they have to prove is a working knowledge of English. This assumes that the knowledge of those on board the ships is adequate but pressures on crews are increasing all the time. Masters are under pressure from owners for quick turnarounds, something which was already worrying Trinity House pilots. If a ship's officer refuses to become 'licensed' to act as pilot for that particular ship, he can be replaced by one who will and who will be prepared to take a certificate of pilotage and become licensed as pilot of that particular vessel.

Some, but not all, Trinity House pilots have been taken on by port authorities but it has been made clear to them that they have no right to protest about anything they are asked to do under the new system and that the port authorities can take on literally anyone they consider to be suitable as a pilot, if needs be at short notice.

'There are ships currently on their way here now', said Mr Foot in August 1988, 'who don't even know they will have to cope with the manoeuvres across the shipping lanes on their own or how to do it.' As they can't go inshore as the Goodwin sands and Dover harbour approaches are too dangerous, their only option is to cross the 'motorway' alone before they pick up a pilot. They will be doing this after having spent weeks at sea on an empty ocean with boundless horizons in water of infinite depth.

'To masters of vessels used to the North Sea trade, in well-found ships with modern technology at their disposal, this calls for navigation with great care. For most vessels, with ill-trained crews under flags of convenience, with faulty equipment and after a month-long passage across empty oceans, it is a recipe for disaster.'

One of the reasons put forward by the government for doing away with the Trinity House pilots was that so many pilots had become unnecessary owing to there being fewer merchant ships and better technology. Yet ships are becoming more and more complex and sophisticated while, at the same time, being crewed by more inexperienced seamen. The 'flagging' of nearly all ships with flags of convenience has become a serious problem.

Those working in the merchant service point out that while captains and chief engineers are still often European or English-speaking, the vast majority of crews are from the Third World – Filipinos, Cape Verde Islanders, Hong Kong Chinese, Indians, Pakistanis and Malays. There is nothing racist in their viewpoint. It is merely that they are concerned that many of them do not speak English nor have they been trained to the high standards of the British Merchant Service. That service is only a fraction of what it once was with only 500 British merchant vessels left, mainly little coasters.

Huge ships come into the Thames. Tankers of 130,000 GRT go into Canvey Island. If you try and stop one quickly, then first you have to stop the engines as it takes minutes before the grip of the water takes place, then you have to reverse them. A 'fast' emergency stop for a loaded ship would take about two minutes, and even after you've put the engines into reverse the ship would carry on going for another three miles! That is exactly the width of the shipping lanes in the narrowest part of the Channel. During this manoeuvre you have no control over the ship. When it does stop it will slew around at a right angle to the direction in which it had been going. The dangers are obvious.

Nine times out of ten, said Mr Foot, 'lane crossing', can be done safely with an experienced pilot and a well-found ship, and with extreme caution. There is traffic steaming down all the time from Hamburg and Holland in the north east while a similar flow comes up the other way. You have to give way to *everything* on your starboard bow, that is the rule of the sea, so this means giving way to ships in their scores sailing out of northern Europe. A heavily-laden, vulnerable ship like a tanker would probably take twenty minutes to cross the sea-lanes and this is where there could be a collision.

The government's view is a simple one. Trinity House pilotage had become too costly. It no longer reflected the need for services.

'I am full of foreboding', said Mr Foot. 'Trinity House pilots had their reputations at stake and if there is an accident you always feel some responsibility – after all, it takes two to make an accident.' And all this to save £33m.

The cost of compensation in the event of a disaster will be infinitely more than this, far outweighing any savings that may be made. Other countries bordering the North Sea have introduced strict traffic safety regulations. We, on the other hand, have ensured cheaper pilotage at the expense of pollution and loss of life. What price progress?

Ro-Ro Ferries

Irrespective of statistics, a single accident to this type of vessel can lead to catastrophic loss of life and the risk of such a consequence is too high.

The Royal Institution of Naval Architects, 21 March 1988

As was noted at the investigation into the sinking of the *Herald of Free Enterprise*, irrespective of the chapter of events which led up to it, there are those who are unhappy anyway about the design of this type of vessel. They include the Royal Institution of Naval Architects and the Nautical Institute.

In March 1988 the Royal Institution of Naval Architects (RINA) published a statement on *The Safety and Vulnerability of Ro-Ro Ships*, prepared by a technical committee of the Institution and endorsed by its full Council.

It states that while recognizing the problems currently facing operators, managers, designers and builders within the shipping industry, the 'Council nevertheless considers it necessary to record its professional opinion on the question of passenger Ro-Ro ship vulnerability in the event of a serious accident'. A series of recent events had given them the impetus to hold a special conference in association with the Nautical Institute and the Institute of Marine Engineers on the whole question of safety and Ro-Ro ferries.

In the light of circumstances which now pertain it is considered that current designs of Ro-Ro passenger ships now in service, despite their full adherence to the law and regulations, are unacceptably vulnerable in that there is a likelihood of rapid capsize under certain conditions, particularly collision. Conventional ships give passengers and crew a reasonable chance of evacuation should such an emergency occur.

The short term actions taken by the Department of Transport following the loss of the *Herald of Free Enterprise* are welcome, particularly in relation to operational practices. The Department, however, has yet to resolve some difficult problems affecting the vulnerability of existing ships, for example:

(a) Dangers of flooding large areas of deck near the waterline
(b) High permeability in some compartments which can therefore admit large volumes of water
(c) The dangers of fire both in the vehicle spaces and in accommodation areas immediately above

(d) The possibility that passengers numbering thousands, ma⸱ not be safely evacuated in a very short time.

Technical solutions to the fundamental problem of rapid capsize following flooding are available now; the means of their enforcement are not. It is indisputable that their implementation will cost money both in capital cost and operational inconvenience but safety must override such considerations.

Longer term research will refine solutions, *but the means of reducing the likelihood of rapid capsize should be adopted now* [my italics]. These include the fitting of door or shutter-type transverse bulkheads on vehicle decks; the judicious use of longitudinal bulkheads; the addition of sponsons or bulges; the reduction of permeability by filling spaces with buoyant material and various similar improvements.

In May 1988 the *Journal of the Nautical Institute* published the Institute's views on the subject. While noting the overall 'exceptionally good' record of the vessels, it states that early designs – that is, those ships built before 1980 – are inherently vulnerable because of their method of construction. They become vulnerable if they sustain a collision, if their cargo shifts or if water enters through an opening.

Julian Parker, of the Nautical Institute, rightly pointed out to the author that no vessel would be likely to have stayed afloat if it sailed with what amounted to a huge hole in it – in the case of the *Herald* caused by the open bow doors. The original Ro-Ro ferries were designed so that their car decks should be just above the water-line so that if the ship was holed, it should stay afloat for thirty minutes. But this, Mr Parker suggested, assumed that the ship was bound to be holed amidships and would stay upright in the water. It did not allow for holes fore and aft which would have quite a different effect – the ship would then be likely to turn over.

The government argues, he said, that there is no fundamental necessity to change the design on the old ships because, by ensuring they are operated safely and kept out of danger, such an accident should never take place. They are determined, therefore, that they shall be loaded, trimmed and sailed in such a way, that they are not vulnerable.

The Nautical Institute's argument however, is that if they do have an accident, these older ships would probably sink and turn over quickly and it is totally wrong for the government to put enormous penalties on the master and crew (£50,000 fines and/or two years imprisonment) in order to ensure the safety of the ships if the inherent design will make them vulnerable to capsize. 'We have our calculations and figures to document this could happen and it is all in our report.'

The institute's report concludes:

Commercial expediency cannot be given as an excuse to absolve governments of their responsibility to the public to ensure that passenger Ro-Ro ferries do not capsize following an incident, before the passengers have a reasonable chance to evacuate the ship. There are three reasons for making this assertion.

(i) There are no practical means of ensuring that two or more vessels will *never* collide.
(ii) The facts are well known, the physical parameters concerning stability and vulnerability can be calculated accurately: there is therefore no justification for not applying the correct principles.
(iii) Ferries generally carry upwards of 500 passengers. Society demands, through passenger regulations, that their ships stay upright for a minimum of thirty minutes. It is known that in certain conditions this standard cannot be achieved with the existing designs.

Simply, therefore, the current position is this. Within existing regulations it is considered acceptable that the large open space of the vehicle deck should be only three inches above the waterline. This, as experts point out, appears to assume that there will always be calm water and that the ship will not be subjected to the normal action of wind and waves – yet a tall Ro-Ro ferry is particularly vulnerable to wind.

The *Herald of Free Enterprise* capsized in shallow water. Had she capsized in deeper water, such as in the middle of the Channel, then there is no doubt that everyone would have been lost because she went down in 90 seconds. The most likely cause of an accident, given that everything in a ship is operating properly, is a collision. There are about 320 ship movements in an average

24-hour period in the Dover Straits (which brings us back to the worries of the ex-Trinity House pilots). As we have already learned, most of those are north-south. The only vessels, until the new pilotage regime was brought in, which regularly crossed the shipping lanes were the cross-channel ferries and, of course, they still do. According to a report on Granada's *World in Action* on 10 October 1988, there have actually been some 21 Ro-Ro ferry collisions in British waters in the last ten years, mostly minor, with the exception of the *European Gateway* in 1982 which, as we know, sank with the loss of 6 lives.

There is no doubt that one way substantially to reduce the risk of immediate capsize is to break up the large open space of the car deck with transverse bulkheads which would divide up the space into compartments. This is no new notion. The 'unsinkable' *Titanic* sank, in part, because her bulkheads did not reach the full depth of the decks.

Apparently when the government commandeered a Ro-Ro ferry, the *Rangatira* for the Falklands War, the Ministry of Defence insisted that two transverse bulkheads were fitted to reduce the risk of flooding. Ironically, these were removed when the ship went back into commercial service.

Since it appeared that neither the Department of Transport nor the ferry companies know what it would cost to put such bulkheads into their ferries, Granada Television commissioned a firm of specialist marine engineers to work it out. Macgregor Navire used a computer to show how two transverse steel bulkheads could be put into existing ships and how this would affect the average loading of cars, caravans and lorries. Making and fitting the doors, they estimated, would costs £115,000 per ferry. The amount of deck space lost as a result would mean that a ferry need only carry two cars, one lorry and six passengers less. They were sure that the time lost at each end of the run would be nil but they fed into the computer that two minutes would be lost each end. The total cost of it all per ferry worked out at £390,000 per ship per year.

If the ferry companies chose to pass the whole cost on – and it appeared from the views of ordinary passengers being interviewed that they would be quite happy to pay more for safety – then, for the companies to recover their outlay over the first twelve months, it would cost only *35p* per person on a single fare between Dover and Calais. If they chose to recover it over four years and take a percentage from vehicles as well, then it would cost 10p per passenger, 48p per car and £1.92 per lorry.

A small price to pay and one which needs to be paid; for, if it is not, and there is a mid-Channel collision (something which becomes more likely without the expertise of the Trinity House pilots guiding foreign ships across the shipping lanes), then the loss of life could dwarf what happened on the *Herald of Free Enterprise*.

It did seem, immediately after Zeebrugge, that the problem had been recognized. Mrs Thatcher, after visiting the survivors, told reporters: 'It is the fundamental design of the ferry that I understand is the problem. A disaster like this has been predicted because of the *design* of the ship.' Yet within days the then Transport Secretary, John Moore, told parliament that the cause of the sinking was that the bow doors had been left open and that 'there is no evidence to suggest this was due to any fault in the fundamental design of the ship'.

We are told that if such modifications are wanted then they will need to be agreed internationally and that this could take years. Following Zeebrugge the government set up a £1m inquiry into the subject – which is not even expected to report before 1992!

Yet international shipping regulations say that a ship is expected to remain afloat for thirty minutes after an accident, to allow everyone time to get off. Ro-Ro ferries sink in seconds.

One marine expert told the Granada TV reporters: 'Air passengers accept that if you have a mid-air collision, you're all dead but no one should have to go aboard a ferry with those feelings.' With so little chance to use the lifeboats a collision would, almost inevitably, be disastrous.

As Julian Parker of the Nautical Institute said to the writer:

> On this one conflicting point we argue that the government can't have it both ways and say 'we'll fine anyone for taking unsafe ships to sea, but we'll allow unsafe ships to *go* to sea . . . '

7 The Channel Tunnel

A thirty-one-mile-long crematorium . .
David Matthews, *Health and Safety Officer, Fire Brigades Union*

NEWS HEADLINE 29 FEBRUARY 1995 – 100 DIE IN
CHANNEL TUNNEL FIRE' is how the Fire Brigades Union
opened its contribution to a special 'Symposium on Safety in the
Channel Tunnel' held in January 1987.

There is growing alarm among experts over the safety of the
tunnel project, a project which has been rushed ahead with
almost unprecedented speed. Nothing has been allowed to stand
in its way. A special hybrid bill was speeded through parliament
to enable construction to go ahead without the usual kind of
public inquiry so massive a project would normally have had to
face – and also to allow cars, cars with caravans, coaches and
commercial vehicles all to be transported in the same enclosed
compartment as people.

The basic design details are these. There will be a 'Fixed Link'
with a total length of 49.2 kilometres (30 miles) of which 37.5
kilometres will be beneath the sea. There will be two running
tunnels 7.3 metres in diameter with a service tunnel in the centre
of 4.5 metres. The interior width of each wagon will be 3.75m,
the track for cars 1.90m and the width left for two walkways,
1.85m. These figures show, according to Robert Blackburn,
OBE, former Chief Fire Officer of West Sussex County Council
and former Fire Adviser to the Home Secretary, 'that the width
at the side of the vehicles will be 0.925m wide – this is less than
the full opening of car doors'.

It is, he continued, the intention to build 150 cross passages at
357 metre intervals to join the running tunnels to the service
tunnels, these to be used among other things, for the evacuation
of people from the shuttle in the event of an emergency. The

passages will be something in the order of 3.3 metres wide and fitted with 1.4 metre wide fire resisting doors.

The 'need' to carry passengers with their cars is economic. If the tunnel is to become remotely profitable it will have to prove a much faster option than the ferries. The consortium of companies who are building the British end of the tunnel, Eurotunnel, has had a monumental task in raising money for the project, even having to go as far afield as the Soviet Union and China to borrow money.

Already deadlines are running behind as unforeseen problems have arisen. The contractors boring the initial tunnel are far behind schedule and Eurotunnel is threatening to claim penalties for delay. As *The Times* reported on 4 August 1988,

> to meet the deadline Trans Manche Link (TML) should bore the service tunnel – the smaller of the three – 5 km out to sea by November 1 1988. But Eurotunnel has complained that the work was up to eight weeks late and had reached only one and a half kilometres. Mr Joe Stacey, Eurotunnel's site manager, said there had been progress recently but the contractors' latest estimate was that they would still be four to five weeks behind the 1 November deadline. Part of the delay had been caused by water in the service tunnel, exposing what Mr Stacey called 'minor design defects' in the 600 ton tunnel-boring machine.

Speed therefore is of the essence.

Earlier in the year the media had carried reports that the five British companies involved in the £5 billion project faced criminal charges instigated by the Health and Safety Executive alleging they had failed to ensure their employees' safety. The prosecution arose from an incident in 1987 when four empty railway wagons broke away and careered out of control to the bottom of the access tunnel, at that time the only way out of the system.

What is worrying the Fire Brigades Union and many other experts is the risk that will be entailed by allowing passengers to travel across the Channel inside their own vehicles. There will be three types of shuttle train – a double-deck unit for cars which will accommodate five cars per deck; a single unit for light commercial units, coaches, cars with caravans, etc.; and a special heavy duty single deck for heavy goods vehicles. The train will be made up of two units of wagons of a particular type which they call Rakes, each of which will consist of thirteen single deck wagons, two Rakes making up one train. Mr R. B. Blackburn estimates that an average train would contain some 200 cars and approximately 1500 passengers.

This is where the whole question of car fires rears its ugly head. In 1973 there were 23,000 car fires. By 1983 this figure had risen to 40,000 (according to Home Office Fire Statistics). Currently the UK Fire Brigades are responding to 46,000–47,000 car fires a year which represent, on average, one fire for every 400 road vehicles registered. Many small outbreaks are not even reported because the drivers or passengers are able to put them out themselves.

As John Butler, M.Sc., lecturer in mechanical and fire engineering at Dublin College of Technology, said: 'The difference between a *large fire* and a *small fire* is usually a matter of luck and time. If a person ignored the arson factor then the majority of car fires occur when the car is being operated or shortly after the vehicle has stopped – usually these are carburettor-involved fires.'

For parked cars, he continued, an investigator would normally consider such causes as a possible leaking fuel tank, smoking materials, children playing with matches, defects in electrical conductors or components as possible sources of ignition. A recent Kent Fire Brigade survey on 'fires in motor vehicles' covering the years 1982–6 indicated that approximately 25 per cent of the car fires attended by the brigade were due to faults developing in vehicles' electrical systems and a further 2 per cent by smokers or children. In the early years of car manufacture, car seat fillings were of wool, flock or animal hair but this is no longer the case.

Also, if some item in the car is recognized by the manufacturer to have failed to meet its requirements, he will make some attempt to rectify this in later designs; or, if the weakness has received widespread publicity, he will request owners to have the item changed – but not all such defective components are replaced. As a result some car owners may be running their cars at risk to themselves – including a fire risk.

Again and again the point is made – on all car ferries, passengers and vehicles are *always* segregated precisely because of fire risk. Sir Kenneth Holland, CBE, formerly Her Majesty's Chief Fire Inspector, said:

> I consider the potential hazard to life is far greater than that of a ship-board situation. For whatever the reason or reasons, it appears to be illogical to ban passengers from the car decks of a Channel ferry boat but to *provide* for them to remain with their vehicles in the much tighter environment of a tunnel-confined railway train.

It will be hot in the tunnel. Those in their vehicles are expected to 'self police' themselves. As they become hot and uncomfortable – particularly if there are any delays due say, to the shuttle ahead breaking down (and this is bound to happen from time to time), then they will be tempted to switch on their radios or use their fans to cool the car – thus activating the car's electrical system. If the driver or adult passengers are smokers they might decide to risk lighting up to while away the time. The fact that adults are present will not guarantee that all children will stop playing with matches if they have access to them.

Caravans provide especial hazards with cooking, heating and refrigeration facilities aboard. These are all run from bottle gas carried inside the caravan. People might well use any delay in the tunnel, or even during the routine passage, to brew up a cup of tea or start to cook. Who will ensure that the liquid gas is turned off in each caravan?

Those going on holiday to the continent, especially if they are camping, pile up their cars with flammable material which often spills on to the roof in roof racks. This too may well include bottles of camping gas. Also, as experts point out, many people fill up with petrol before crossing the Channel so that there will be more full tanks than usual.

Dr H. S. Eisner, M.Sc., PhD. formerly director of the Explosion and Flame Laboratory of the Health and Safety Executive and currently editor of the *Journal of Occupational Accidents*, spelled it out: 'The foolishness of a single football drunk may have greater consequences than the self-policing of a hundred sober citizens can prevent.' In addition, he pointed out, fire could start in one of the two electric trolley locomotives that drive each shuttle.

Other sources of fire include derailment or a shuttle rubbing at high speed against tunnel walls and the power cables slung along them; spillage or leakage of fuel from vehicles which would liberate clouds of petrol vapour inside the wagons; and, finally and most sinister, the possibility of terrorist action.

So – what would happen? According to Dr Eisner, what distinguishes a tunnel fire from others is its greater length and that fresh air can only be brought in, and poisonous fumes extracted, at the two tunnel entrances in England and France.

> In this it resembles a mining rather than a railway tunnel system and any method of fire prevention needs to be based on the – sadly – large experience in this field which has seen many three-figure fatality disasters – the latest being the Kinross Gold Mine disaster in South Africa in 1986, claiming 177 victims.

Once started, he said, a tunnel fire can spread very rapidly; most of the heat goes into raising the temperature of the air that passes through it and downwind temperatures of 1000°C are common. This is passed on to any flammable material in its path and in this way a fire can jump considerable tunnel lengths. 'Moreover, in the peculiar vertical configuration of the Tunnel which runs about 100m below its entries, a fire would exert a powerful "chimney" effect on the ventilation and can cause it to increase, reduce and even reverse.'

A single car catching fire could spread that fire to the next one and so on. In the open, said Dr Eisner, cars that catch fire usually burn themselves out, contrary to what we see on TV. They do not usually explode. But in a confined space it is not uncommon for a violent explosion to take place which, in the tunnel, could be sufficient to blow out the various fire and smoke-resistant doors that are supposed to separate one wagon from the next. 'An increasingly violent spread of fire throughout the wagons of a shuttle could then be expected and blast and fumes emerge into the tunnel proper, the fumes spreading through it at the mercies of whatever ventilation regime happens to prevail at the time. Both running tunnels would be affected because they are linked.'

Currently the idea is that if there was a fire, whoever discovered it would tell the train staff who would then, in turn, advise the control centre by radio. It is considered that even if the train was on fire it would continue along the tunnel if the leading train driver considered it practicable.

Yet the time it takes for smoke inside a burning car to become unbearable is a short one. People inside their cars seeing smoke coming from under the bonnet are likely to panic. They will try to get out. But, as we have already seen, there is not enough room for them to be able to open their car doors fully and if they open them as far as they can, this will block the means of escape for any flow of people trying to get out from behind. If the flow is in the opposite direction people will try and push them closed to get by. Smoke will by that time be filling the wagon and, as the exit door is opened, smoke will spread into the tunnel itself.

People on the top deck of the double-decker car carriers will have an appalling job trying to escape from the top of the wagon. Some people will be trying to climb from the lower level upwards, while those on top will try and climb down to escape. It will be hard enough for the fit and able people to escape down vertical and retractable fire ladders but where will that leave the old, infirm, disabled, children, and mothers with babies in arms?

And all this in dense smoke. David Matthews of the Fire Brigades Union pointed out that even experienced firemen can become totally disorientated in dense smoke and once they have turned around two or three times do not know which direction they are facing. Only recently has it been decided to put signs on the walls of the tunnel saying which end is France and which England.

For those who do manage to get off the wagon there will then be a possible 178m (202 yard) journey before they reach an opening into the service tunnel.

David Matthews was also extremely doubtful whether breathing equipment currently exists which would allow firemen to go further than three miles into the tunnel – or even if Fire Brigades will be used. It is possible that private fire fighting services may be employed by the tunnel companies. The French Fire Brigades do not know what the situation is either.

Mr Blackburn spelled it out:

The travel distance is far in excess of any travel distances considered as reasonable for the escape of people from fire and this is assuming that the tunnel itself is a safe area which is very questionable, unless immediate action has been taken either to contain the fire or to extinguish it in the compartment itself.

Ventilation and the speed of air movement will be a major problem for this project without a fire situation. Superimpose a shuttle fire then the situation will be critical. The safety document talks about a decision being made to decide which way ventilation will be directed. But how will such a decision be made and by whom, based on what information? All present safety plans rely too much on the action of different people not trained to respond to emergencies.

What will be needed to try and avert the worst consequences of a tunnel fire is the separating of people and vehicles, with the vehicles put into fire-resisting carriages with smoke-sealed doors which are kept closed and with the carriage fitted with an automatic fire extinguishing system. People should be carried in special carriages at the front of the train. Then, in the event of a fire, automatic detection and extinguishment could take place and, as Mr Blackburn said,

> at the worst if the fire was not held, the carriage affected could be taken to a fire fighting 'stage' and be uncoupled for the fire services to deal with. The carriages with people could then continue safely out of the tunnel and not rely on an evacuation time estimated at 25 minutes to the Service Tunnel and a total evacuation time of 90 minutes.

> The safety procedures presented by Eurotunnel would, in the event of a serious fire, present the Fire Service with an almost impossible task of rescue work and firefighting with great risk to personnel.

David Matthews, for the Fire Brigades Union, mused on whether some kind of level of 'acceptable deaths' is not built into current planning and costing if the present system is allowed to go ahead for, if there was a serious fire the imaginary headline at the beginning of this chapter is likely to be an underestimate.

Sir Keith Holland felt that whatever the economic reasons for non-segregation might be, 'I cannot envisage any social benefits of non-segregation. It would seem to be unlikely that any economic advantages of non-segregation would be acceptable to society as off-setting the much lower standard of safety from fire inherent in such a situation.'

Dr Eisner was even more blunt:

> The hazard from an outbreak of fire in the Channel Tunnel is not that, sooner or later it *will* happen, but that *when* it does, the lives of a very large number of people will be put at risk by a single event. At peak times over 2000 passengers and staff may find themselves inside the twin-tunnel system, with double that number envisaged by the turn of the century.

We cannot say we have not been warned.

8 Going Critical – Nuclear Power

The safest form of energy known to man...
Energy Secretary Peter Walker (17 March 1986),
five weeks before Chernobyl

It was only one of the bizarre features of the Layfield Inquiry into the building of a pressurized water reactor (PWR) at Sizewell in Suffolk that, although the accident at Chernobyl occurred during that inquiry, mention of what had happened was not allowable nor considered necessary to the inquiry's subsequent findings – not that the result had ever been in any doubt.

Now, with another such inquiry under way at Hinkley Point in Somerset the same kind of arguments are being put forward – that we could not have a Chernobyl-type accident here. In its submission to that inquiry the Central Electricity Generating Board (CEGB) calculate the chances of dying from the results of a nuclear accident at Hinkley at around one chance in five million years. For some types of accident this figure rockets to one chance in ten thousand million years, so confident is the organization about the safety of this new design of PWR reactor.

Not everyone feels so sanguine. In the aftermath of Chernobyl James Asseltine, head of the US Nuclear Regulatory Commission, said on 27 May 1986: 'I have had to advise Congress that there is a forty-five per cent chance of another serious nuclear accident within the next twenty years.' If we look at past history there have been three major nuclear accidents in thirty years (and that does not count the mysterious explosion in the Urals in 1957 about which we still know little except that stored nuclear waste apparently blew up) – and two in seven years, at Three Mile Island and Chernobyl.

In their praise for the flawless design of their new reactor the CEGB do mention that 'these studies do not quantify the risk from such factors as human intervention and internal and external hazards . . . ', and in fact they have made much in their publicity about virtually eliminating human error. Yet human error has been at the base of all nuclear accidents, major and minor, because human beings design nuclear reactors and build them and operate them and, human beings being only fallible, they make mistakes.

It is not possible to go into great detail here about the three worst accidents – Windscale, Three Mile Island and Chernobyl – but a brief history of what happened is necessary in order to explain possible future risks. Also it is significant to look at the way governments reacted to them.

The fact is still played down that until Chernobyl, our own home-grown accident at Windscale in 1957 was the world's worst nuclear accident. This lack of knowledge was partly due to the fact that it took thirty years for most of the information on what happened to become known, a fact which made the berating of the Soviet Union for keeping quiet about Chernobyl for three or four days particularly hypocritical. Over the amount of radiation released for example – we were continually informed this was minimal and, anyway, was blowing out across the Irish Sea. In the event 376,000 curies of radioactivity from forty radioactive isotopes were released over two days, on 10 and 11 October. This was almost a thousand times greater than the amount of radioactivity released at Three Mile Island.

It was in 1948 that a group of visiting American experts warned the operators at Windscale of something called the 'Wigner expansion' effect in the graphite planned for use in the reactors. This caused the design to be modified because American physicist Edward Teller (the 'father of the H-bomb') had warned that if the Wigner energy was not released by regularly heating up the graphite, it could cause a fire in a fuel rod which could trigger off a major disaster.

The accident, when it occurred, was caused by an experienced physicist in what was described later as a moment of aberration. One of the plutonium producing reactors threw a switch too soon as the physicist was carrying out a Wigner release.

According to his instruments he thought the temperature in the core was falling without completing the release and as he did not have an operating manual handy which would tell him what to do in such circumstances nor sufficiently detailed instructions, he decided to give the power level another short boost to bring the temperature back up and complete the release. What he did not know was that the instruments recording the temperature down in the core of the reactor were not in the hottest part of it and that the temperatures therefore varied. When, at 11.05 a.m. he withdrew the control rods to raise the power of the reactor again, the additional unnoticed rise in temperature ignited at least one of the rods.

He had no idea anything was wrong. Not until 5.40 a.m. on 10 October – 42 hours and 35 minutes later – was there any indication that there was anything amiss inside the core of No. 1 reactor. The instruments then showed radioactivity reaching the filters on the top of the air-discharge cooling stack – known as 'Cockcroft's folly' after Sir John Cockcroft who had insisted the stack should be built when many had considered it unnecessary. 'Cockcroft's folly' saved an all-out catastrophe. By this time the staff realized something had gone terribly wrong, the raging fire in the reactor was spreading and nobody was sure what to do. They tried to put it out with carbon dioxide coolant but that only fanned the flames.

It was not until 11 October, when the fire had been raging for 24 hours, that the chief constable of Cumberland was informed there might be a full-scale emergency. Gradually the fire was brought under control with water. Also on 11 October the wind, which had indeed been blowing over the Irish Sea, turned and blew back inland. One of the most immediate effects of such an accident is the immediate release of iodine-131 which gets into the food chain, via grass and milk, and lodges in the thyroid. For four days local people drank contaminated milk before the order went out to pour it away and some two million litres of milk had to be destroyed. Some 20,000 curies of iodine-131 had been released.

The then prime minister, Harold Macmillan, ordered that the accident should be played down and it was. It was twenty-six years before any significant facts came out and longer still before all the details emerged. A study published by the National Radiological Protection Board (NRPB) estimated there would probably have been about 20 cancer deaths as a result and possibly some 230 thyroid cancers. But there were other substances emitted, like polonium, which would raise the figure and the NRPB later amended their estimate to 33 deaths, although independent experts would put it higher than that.

On the 16 March 1979 a Hollywood thriller opened at one of the main New York cinemas. It was called *The China Syndrome*, and starred Jack Lemmon as the manager of a nuclear power station, with a pressurized water reactor, where there was a major accident, and Jane Fonda as the reporter who exposed the cover-up. It was a box office hit. (The 'China syndrome' is the term given to a theoretical circumstance where, following a core meltdown in a reactor, a mass of radioactive material goes through the earth's core – in the case of the USA it would end up in China . . .)

After seeing the previews, the American nuclear industry rushed out statements to the effect that it was an impossible fairy story which could never happen. Just twelve days later, on 28 March, it did.

The building of the twin reactors had been rushed through on an island in the Susquehanna River, ten miles south-east of Harrisburg in Pennsylvania. They were to be operated by the Metropolitan Edison Company, who had been proposing a similar nuclear station in New Jersey, but this had run into a lot of problems so a new site was needed in haste. Building commenced after the briefest of public hearings.

As is ever the way with building nuclear plants, costs escalated frighteningly above budget. Unit 1 was supposed to have cost $110m but this rose to $400m by the time it was completed and Unit 2 cost nearly $700m. Costs had to be cut, therefore, in operating the units. One way to cut costs is to keep the reactor running and on stream almost continually, as shutting it down vastly increases expense. So the idea is to shut it down only for refuelling which encourages those running it to delay repairs until such a shutdown. No plant operator would want a reactor out of service for any length of time while, for instance, comprehensive safety checks were made or new safety systems installed.

Three Mile Island is instructive as to future policy here – it was run by a private company which had to maximize its profits. It persuaded federal safety officials that adequate checks on safety could be carried out while the reactor was actually operating, which is rather like saying you can check out an aircraft while it is in flight.

In October 1977 a faulty piece of equipment was discovered. Water entering the reactor had to pass through special tanks known as 'polishers', which filtered out impurities through special filters made of thousands of tiny resin beads. There were eight polishers, only seven being needed when the reactor was actually running. Every twenty-eight days the beads had to be changed for clean ones and sludge cleaned out of the bottom of the tanks.

It was later found that the polishers were exempt from federal safety rules, that plant officials did not have accurate drawings for the Unit 2 polisher system, that those they did have showed valves in the wrong places, improperly identified components and had air-line positions and interconnections incorrectly displayed. It also transpired there were long gaps between cleaning out the sludge from the tanks and replacing the beads and that on numerous occasions, when this was done, there had been serious problems. No attempt was made to overcome them although it had been known for seventeen months before the accident that a blockage in the system could cause an accident.

On 19 October 1977 an engineer cleaning out the beads from Polisher 2 found a water leak, followed by the unexpected closure of a set of valves in the system cutting off the main feedwater system completely. Fortunately the Unit 2 reactor was not working at the time. An internal memo noted that had it been, there would have been severe problems. The memo recommended nine safety measures to ensure it did not happen again. They were all rejected out of hand by the director of the start-up operations, R. J. Toole, who wrote 'no further action required' across the memo.

On 12 May 1978 the valves slammed shut again and again cut off the water supply system. Again the operators were lucky that the reactor was not running. A shift supervisor, William Zewe, wrote another memo on 15 May saying something had to be done 'before a very serious accident occurs.' He suggested a means whereby a fast-acting automatic by-pass system could be installed which would keep the water running should the valves stick again. Nothing was done.

Later it was also to come out that the training of staff and their qualifications were less than adequate. No one on duty at the time of the accident was a qualified nuclear engineer or even a college graduate. Operators were taught only how to carry out routine operations. Nobody had any training in what to do in the event of a complicated accident, not even the plant supervisors.

On 28 March 1979, it was not third time lucky for Metropolitan Edison. When the same series of mishaps in the polishing tanks occurred again the reactor in Unit 2 was operating flat out at 97 per cent capacity. First a small pipe from one of the eight polishers clogged up. The polishers were in the process of being cleaned, the sludge removed and new resin beads put in. Just before 4 a.m. the Unit 2 shift foreman checked how the work on the blocked pipe was going. Suddenly, as in *The China Syndrome*, he heard a loud thundering noise 'like a couple of freight trains'. Over the loudspeaker came the words 'Turbine trip, reactor trip'. The maintenance men had blocked the flow of water to the main feedwater system, forcing the turbine and reactor to shut down.

Immediate supposedly failsafe emergency measures were taken. The devices were linked to the electronic alert system and were supposed to trigger off remedial action in the event of an accident, including any interruption of the main feedwater system. In addition three emergency pumps were supposed to start up in the event of an accident, but things just kept on going wrong.

The nuclear reactor reacted immediately to the shutdown of its water supply. The pressure of the coolant water inside it increased rapidly since it was still being heated by the uranium. A surge of pressure blew open a relief valve, one that should have closed after a few seconds. Instead it stuck open. Coolant water rushed out of the reactor at the rate of 220 gallons a minute. This happened because someone had shut off two valves that carried water from the emergency pumps into the cooling system so that the three emergency pumps failed to work!

The result of all this was the supposedly 'incredible' multiple safety system failure which the nuclear industry says cannot happen. There were still three more pumps connected to a special emergency reservoir capable of resupplying the reactor with a thousand gallons of water a minute to replace that being drained off. Two minutes after the accident the pumps came on automatically but the operators in the control room who were monitoring the accident shut them off two minutes later. They quite simply did not believe what they saw on the monitor screens so deliberately overrode the plant's own safety back-up equipment. Then they compounded their error by opening a pipe to remove *even more* water, doubling the amount lost . . .

The operators, trying to cope with an accident for which they were totally untrained, had taken the instrument readings to mean the reactor had too much water in it, not too little. They did not know the valve was stuck open until the supervisor for the morning shift arrived and guessed what had happened. There were no gauges to tell operators how much water there was in the reactor, they had to guess by monitoring another tank linked to its cooling system. Since their instruments told them the tank was full, they assumed the reactor was full too.

Five minutes after the failure of its feedwater system, the reactor began to tear itself apart. The water remaining turned to steam which expanded and knocked out its control rods, finally preventing any possible cooling. There then followed a whole series of instrument, equipment and computer failures. 'It seemed to go on and on, surprise after surprise', said radiation protection supervisor Thomas Mulleavy afterwards.

At 7.24 a.m. the station manager declared a General Emergency, the first ever at an American nuclear plant. For sixteen hours the uranium remained inadequately cooled, large amounts of radioactivity were released from the fuel rods and escaped through the open valve into the building housing the reactor, and thousands of gallons of radioactive water were accidentally pumped into an insecure neighbouring building.

Officials assured everyone that nothing much had happened, it was all under control. High radiation readings were merely 'oddball instrument error'. Two days later Nuclear Regulatory Commission experts admitted to being 'dumbfounded' at the number of equipment failures. A plume of radioactive gas floated over neighbouring towns while inside the damaged reactor a large, growing, and potentially explosive 'hydrogen bubble' had formed which nobody knew how to cope with. By Friday the bubble was estimated at a size of 1800 cubic feet with a hydrogen content of 4 per cent. It was thought that if it reached 10 per cent it could blow up. 'The bubble was a complete surprise', said Dr Levine of the Brookhaven National Laboratory. Three Mile Island was just full of surprises.

This time Metropolitan Edison were in luck. The bubble decreased in size on its own. Five days after the start of the accident the emergency was over, largely through good luck. It has been estimated that the core of the reactor came within 30 minutes of a full metldown. The emergency showed up the lack of planning for such an event – there were insufficient supplies of potassium iodate needed to counteract the effects of iodine-131; plans for evacuation were inadequate. The state governor, off his own bat, ordered the closure of all schools and told pregnant women and children within a five-mile radius to leave the area. Plans were finally put in hand to evacuate 165,000 people living within a ten-mile radius. In the event, 140,000 did not wait but took to the roads regardless, clogging the highways in every direction.

Nobody came well out of the subsequent public hearings. The final report ripped apart the power utilities, the Nuclear Regulatory Commission and everyone else for 'being unable to provide an acceptable level of safety in nuclear power'. It was widely said at the time that no one had suffered as a result of the accident but there now appears to be a rising number of cancers in the area and, indeed, in the summer following the accident, infant mortality in Pennsylvania rose by an unprecedented 92 per cent.

They called the Three Mile Island accident 'the night we nearly lost Pennsylvania'.

Two months before the Chernobyl accident, the magazine *Soviet Life* ran a massive spread on the Chernobyl complex, headlined

'Total Safety'. The reactor was constructed in such a way, it said, that a total meltdown 'was incredible'.

Very briefly, the details are as follows. The Soviet reactor was of a design not used in the West. It is known as an 'RBMK'. In the days immediately following the accident we were told in the West that the design was so patently unsafe that nobody over here would contemplate such a plant. This view was to be somewhat modified in the weeks that followed. We were also told that the RBMK had no secondary containment to contain the spread of radioactivity. It had. We were told that all our reactors had secondary containment. In fact, many of the older sort do not as it was not considered necessary at that time (a point that this writer, among many others, made after Chernobyl).

However good or bad the design though, Chernobyl occurred largely as a result of human error. Just after 1 a.m. on 26 April 1986 the reactor was operating at only 7 per cent power, 'ticking over like an idling car', is how it has been described. It was still capable though of generating a colossal 200 megawatts of heat inside its core.

What appears to have happened is that a group of technicians, blasé about running the reactor, removed or partially removed one or more of the control rods while the reactor was still operating, thinking that nothing could go wrong. Forty seconds after they did so the reactor was racked by a massive surge of power, from 7 per cent to 50 per cent in ten seconds. This surge triggered the destruction of the reactor.

There followed a rapid series of uncontrollable events, leading in the end to the destruction of No. 4 reactor. As explained in *The Worst Accident in The World*, by a number of the *Observer*'s specialists,

> Its double containment was now breached and the top of its core had been smashed open by the impact . . . broken pressure tubes were no longer providing coolant to the top of the core which continued to overheat triggering further reactions between the steam that now poured over the reactor's zirconium and its red-hot blocks of graphite. The graphite itself caught fire and began pouring plumes of highly radioactive fission products such as lanthanum-140, ruthenium-103, caesium-137, iodine-131, tellerium-132, strontium-89, strontium-90 and yytrium-91 which

Soviet scientists later found contaminating the surrounding countryside. The cloud escaped through a gaping hole in the reactor roof and out into the night.

The Soviet authorities, after several days of silence and/or misleading information, then provided exemplary detail of what was going on. Those who fought the fire in the reactor, the nearest man has ever come to a full-blown China syndrome, were brave to the point of their own deaths, from the divers who went down into the cooling ponds beneath the reactor to the pilots who flew aircraft over it, dropping material on to it to dowse the fires. 50,000 people had to be evacuated from the town of Chernobyl, 24,000 from the nearby town of Pripyat. A zone of death was declared within a radius of 19 miles of Chernobyl.

About 30 people died quickly as a result of the accident, either plant or rescue workers. According to official estimates it will kill up to 2,000 people in Europe (including about 50 in Britain) and 45,000 people in the Soviet Union over the next twenty or so years. Ernest Sternglass, radiology professor at Pittsburgh University, considers this could be an underestimate and the overall world death toll could eventually exceed a million.

The reaction in this country showed just how totally unprepared we were for such an eventuality. On 29 April, before anyone could possibly know, Mrs Thatcher robustly told the House of Commons during Question Time that there would be no danger from radioactivity in Britain. However, the world's weather system does not come under the control of the British parliament and on 2 May the radioactive cloud reached here.

The information put out by the experts, including the NRPB, was contradictory and totally confusing. I, myself, tried for hours on the weekend of 5/6 May to get through to them and was eventually told by a spokesman that there was no hazard – no, he said, they could not say which radioactive substances had been released and anyway try the Department of the Environment.

They were busy passing the buck elsewhere. They released information about the amount of radioactivity in a square metre of grass – but what kind of grass? How long is a piece of string? The monitoring systems turned out to be a complete shambles. What eventually became apparent was that some areas of the country, particularly in the north and west, received very high levels of radiation. Equally unbelievable were the statements that it would all pass away within days, unbelievable because the substances themselves had such long half-lives. In fact eighteen months later more than 700 farms in Cumbria, Wales, Scotland and Northern Ireland were still affected by restrictions on sheep movement because of radiation from the accident, a figure which has reduced little in the two-and-a-half years since. Worst of all we were told it was safe for children to drink milk and it is now likely that dozens of children throughout the country will contract thyroid cancer as a result.

The foregoing are just the three most spectacular accidents – there have been hundreds more worldwide, with over three hundred at our own reprocessing plant of Sellafield (ex-Windscale) alone. Nuclear power has become a dicey issue. The programme has virtually ground to a halt in the USA and in much of Europe with only Britain, France and the Soviet Union pressing on in this part of the world and Japan in the Far East.

Nuclear reactors are ageing. In Britain we have a number of our older Magnox-type which have passed what might be described as their 'sell by' date. The Nuclear Installations Inspectorate (NII) has been unhappy with some of them for a considerable while – Berkeley, Bradwell, Trawsfynydd in North Wales, Hunterston A in Scotland, Hinkley A, Sizewell A and Dungeness A. In the summer of 1988 it was finally decided that Berkeley, at least, should be closed down – leaving the problem of decommissioning to be sorted out. This will have to be a process of learning as we go as no one has yet fully decommissioned a nuclear power station.

The Japanese government is rethinking its nuclear power programme after a series of mishaps with ageing nuclear reactors which have caused them considerable problems. They, also, will shortly be faced with a similar dilemma.

Therefore, in Britain we have both the problem of keeping our ageing reactors safe and of preventing any kind of major accident when the new PWRs come on stream.

In its evidence to the Hinkley Point inquiry, the CEGB explained how it has worked out the possibility of accidents by using what is termed the concept of the 'Design Based Accident' (DBA) and claimed that the new PWRs are designed to the highest fool-proof standards – which is, no doubt, quite true. The twin aims of the board is to ensure 'that those accidents which in practical terms could conceivably happen have consequences which can be accepted and that those accidents which have unacceptable consequences will not occur'.

Leaving aside for the moment the question of what is acceptable and to whom, the concept of the Design Based Accident has severe limitations, as spelled out by the evidence also submitted to the Hinkley Point inquiry by COLA, the large consortium of county and local authorities on specialist advice. The DBA is a means, it says, by which the operator may prepare the overall safety case, postulate all foreseeable accidents and demonstrate the adequacy of the support and safety systems to control all such accidents. When an accident scenario extends outside this scenario, then the plant and/or support system design is modified accordingly.

The CEGB undertakes this by progressively modifying the design until either the accident is rendered absolutely impossible or by implementing such modifications and systems that render the scenario of the accident sufficiently remote to make a future occurrence improbable or by providing such systems and safeguards to render its consequences 'acceptable'.

The CEGB also applies another set of calculations called Probabilistic Risk Assessment (PRA) to possible plant-initiated fault sequences. So, as COLA points out, the concept of a Design Based Accident relies upon the validity of the Probabilistic Risk Assessment as a technique for quantifying the risks involved and assumes that all such risks can *be* quantified.

But these techniques have inherent flaws. It is just not possible to postulate all future nuclear plant accidents and malfunctions owing to the complexity of the plant itself; it is not possible to be absolutely certain that all components are as good as they should be and are corrrectly fitted (the nuclear industry has a history of crazy component installations, including some put in back to front or upside down); because of the unique technology of nuclear power and the catastrophic consequences of severe accidents, there is little past data on which to draw so that in many cases it is necessary to use subjective judgement to estimate fault probabilities; Probabilistic Risk Assessment is applied as an absolute standard whereas it is recognized that it is more reliable in comparison with similar systems and, when it is applied to accident scenarios it indicates only the *chance* of an accident, not *when* it might happen.

Lastly it does not adequately incorporate human factors and human failings. In fact the CEGB's approach to safety is based almost entirely upon engineering considerations. These may, as the COLA documents point out, be proof against the adverse consequence of single failures of components or of operators but such engineered defences offer little protection against combinations of human failure, particularly those which originate in the organizational and managerial sections.

Which is where we come to the hub of the problem of risk and why it was necessary to tell, briefly, the stories of Windscale, Three Mile Island and Chernobyl. All, at the end of the day, occurred due to human error. A physicist undergoes a 'moment of aberration', makes a mistake and there follows the Windscale fire. Cost cutting and the refusal to act on recommendations to ensure that there is a system whereby the main water supply to the reactor at Three Mile Island is kept flowing sets in motion a train of events which leads to a whole series of equipment failures, compounded by the fact that when the emergency arose the panic-stricken operatives did the wrong things. At Chernobyl operatives experimented with the fuel rods for reasons we shall never know, just as we shall never know why three American operatives similarly interfered with the fuel rods at the Idaho Falls reactor in 1961 – their extremely radio-active remains had to be scraped off the floors and ceiling and buried in lead-lined boxes.

The CEGB, in its Hinkley Point evidence, quotes what the inspector at the Sizewell B inquiry, Sir Frank Layfield, QC, concluded *after* Chernobyl:

> An accident at Sizewell B, if built, would almost certainly have tolerable consequences, at worst requiring measures such as the banning of milk near the station. Theoretically possible accidents which could cause hundreds or thousands of deaths would almost certainly not occur. (Layfield Report, par. 2 126 (d))

This is a remarkable statement; 'tolerable consequences' – tolerable to whom? To Sir Frank who lives miles away, to the CEGB in the headquarters in London? To the people living in nearby Leiston? While James Asseltine, head of the USA's Nuclear Regulatory Inspectorate – and presumably a world expert – says there is a 45 per cent chance of another major accident occurring within the next twenty years, Sir Frank who is not a nuclear expert says that 'theoretically possible' major accidents 'would almost certainly not occur'. Note the use of the word 'almost'.

Our government and nuclear industry were loud in their criticism of the measures taken by the Russians after Chernobyl. Yet they managed to evacuate the enormous total of 135,000 people from the nineteen-mile 'zone of death' round the crippled reactor within days, and within hours had distributed potassium iodate tablets (the antidote to the thyroid-seeking radionuclides like strontium-90) to everyone living nearby.

Compare this with what we know of our plans for such an emergency, plans which are considered by some members of our own Nuclear Installations Inspectorate to be grossly inadequate, according to a report in *The Independent* (10 August 1988).

In spite of the fact that areas of upland Britain are still suffering from the effects of Chernobyl, an accident which occurred well over two years ago and thousands of miles away, our own plans envisage only evacuating at risk populations two to three kilometres from the boundary fence of a nuclear plant, a fact greeted with somewhat incredulous amusement by the Soviet fire chief, General-Major Mikeev, at a seminar on 17 September 1987. Large stocks of potassium iodate are not necessarily held near to nuclear plants – and one scenario proposed by the government in a circular issued to general practitioners in 1985 said these would be distributed, if necessary, by the local police. It also suggested that those 'caught outside' in the event of an accident should wash off the fallout by 'taking a shower' . . . ! (advice for GPs in the event of a nuclear emergency, DHSS and NRPB Annex. B.HC (85)24 – supplement to HC(77)1, July 1985).

To return to the Nuclear Installations Inspectors; they consider that plans drawn up for an emergency are 'inconsistent, uncoordinated and unsatisfactory'. Neither the Inspectorate nor its parent organization, the Health and Safety Executive, has the legal powers it needs to ensure that emergency plans are satisfactory.

Four years ago the government, moved by growing criticism, required local authorities to produce emergency plans to deal with the consequences of possible chemical accidents, accidents similar to that which occurred at Flixborough. The deadline was 1 October 1985 but, at the time of writing, only five out of eleven local authorities with nuclear installations in their areas have published any nuclear emergency plans.

A survey of fire stations in those areas, undertaken recently by the Fire Brigades Union, showed that in some instances local fire brigade personnel had never even been allowed inside the nuclear plants, that their equipment was grossly inadequate for tackling a fire at a nuclear reactor, and that some of that equipment was kept so far away that it would take an hour to get it to the site. 'Government money' for providing proper equipment 'was very scarce', said one station.

An NII inspector, who wished to remain anonymous, told *The Independent* that in the event of an accident nobody has any executive responsibility for co-ordinating emergency action outside the nuclear site itself. It was not even clear who would take the decision as to whether or not people should be evacuated. The task of organizing such an evacuation would fall on the police who would, in turn, take their instructions from the Home Office – 'but the Home Office has no responsibility whatsoever under current arrangements', continued the inspector. 'Whose duty is it to plan what happens off-site in a nuclear incident? No one's.'

The only legal responsibility for emergency planning in the nuclear industry lies with the operator of a nuclear power station who has to draw up an *on-site* emergency plan. Local authorities have no statutory duty to co-ordinate the various emergency services and there is no way in law that a conscientious local authority could recoup from the nuclear operators the money it might have to spend in drawing up such plans.

Nor is there any requirement to inform the general public living nearby what they should do in the event of an accident, although in principle there should be some kind of plan available for them to see in the local public library. In the USA telephone directories for areas near nuclear power stations carry detailed instructions as to what to do in the event of an accident.

It is quite clear from the foregoing that what planning there is, is based on moving a few hundred people two or three miles; yet, as was shown at Chernobyl, a major accident would require moving tens of thousands of people hundreds of miles and there is no provision whatsoever in this country for doing that. Sir Frank Layfield's optimistic forecast that the worst we might expect is that local milk supplies might have to be thrown away is simply ludicrous. A major nuclear accident in this overcrowded island would mean thousands of people would have to be permanently resettled miles away from their homes, with all that that means in terms of total disruption; while the effects on agriculture and land in the long term are more or less incalculable.

It is also apparent from the scale of the proposals that we are operating on what might be described as the 'crossed fingers' approach – crossing our fingers in the hope it may never happen. If a major accident occurs and the paucity of the measures proposed to deal with it are fully revealed, it will then be too late to set up something better. The task undertaken by the Russians at Chernobyl was truly Herculean and required massive resources in manpower and specialist equipment.

A major nuclear accident in this country would be different in degree to any other possible disaster. Zeebrugge and Piper Alpha each caused between one hundred and two hundred deaths, a terrible tragedy for the victims and their families. Thirty-one died at King's Cross. But the toll of deaths resulting from these does not continue to rise over the next twenty years; and large areas of countryside did not require to be cleared of people.

Is it worth it? Moreover the possible scenario of a major accident does not even take into account the so far unresolved problem of how we get rid of all the nuclear waste from power stations; or the admitted incidence of cancers and leukaemias around nuclear plants (in some cases from eight to ten times above the national average) which those plants cannot be 'proved' to have caused – so far.

So to the concept of 'acceptable' or 'tolerable' deaths. The way to consider this was very well put by the then science editor of the *Guardian*, Anthony Tucker, in an article he wrote for that paper in May 1986, in the wake of Chernobyl.

> Among the children now playing there is a scattered and unidentifiable group, several times larger, at whose necks the Chernobyl cancer pistol is now unwaveringly pointing. Earlier accidents, even though the scale was smaller, provide an indication of health significance. Recent dose commitment calculations for measurements made at the time of the Windscale reactor fire in 1957 indicate that, averaged over twenty years after the accident, the incidence of thyroid cancer in Britain will have risen by about one per cent. This may sound small, an additional risk of only one in ten million, but it means that about twenty people, most of them children at the time of the accident, were not, and are not 'at some slight risk'. After great distress and sickness, years later – they are dead!

The man who chaired the subsequent inquiry into what happened at Three Mile Island, Chairman Kemeny, says

> we heard the words 'mind set' over and over again in our hearings and this tells us something about the attitudes that led to that accident. The first is that the Nuclear Regulatory Commission and the portion of the industry we examined seemed to be hypnotised by their equipment. Indeed, we found that, overall, their equipment was very good although some could be improved. But we are convinced that if the equipment had been the only problem, we wouldn't be sitting here today.

By 'mind set' he meant a psychological state of mind where those who think in a certain way cannot believe that there is any possibility that they might be wrong.

A final postscript – on 8 October 1988 the Soviet newspaper, *Pravda*, announced that the town of Chernobyl was to be destroyed. The radiation levels there are still so high that the Soviet authorities estimate it would be decades before it would be safe for its previous inhabitants to return to their homes.

9 Pollution – the Slow Burning Fuse

> It's we Conservatives who are not merely friends of the earth – we are its guardians and trustees for generations to come.
>
> *The Prime Minister, Margaret Thatcher,*
> *the Conservative Party Conference, Brighton 1988*

Stirring stuff that . . . and it was the second time that the Prime Minister had announced her commitment to environmental issues. Why, therefore, is Britain known as the dirty man of Europe? The Prime Minister also told us, 'given our record we are well placed to take the lead with other governments in practical efforts to protect the wider world'. Just what is this record?

The subject matter of this chapter is, obviously, very different from that of the foregoing ones. Collisions at sea or in mid-air, a fire in the Channel Tunnel, an accident at a nuclear power station, all are single, dramatic events. Here we turn to the kind of disasters which we might well face from the slow seepage of toxic or nuclear waste, the ever-increasing amounts of pesticides in food and nitrates in water and the hole in the ozone layer. These are all slow to show up and hard to prove – which is why those who continue to disregard all warnings as to the consequences of increasing pollution are so easily able to get away with it.

Toxic Waste

Although in organizations like Friends of the Earth we have some of the finest expertise in the world on the effects of pollution, and although the number of people aware of the problem is slowly growing, yet still, as a nation, we are extremely unsophisticated and ignorant about its dangers compared to most other European countries and the United States.

Many people simply don't care – as instanced in a small way by our increasingly filthy streets, which appear to many to be preferable to spending more money from the rates on cleansing. (What was that we heard once upon a time from the Prime Minister about her pledge to see clean streets again . . . ?) For a very long time those who did sound warnings about the hazards of toxic waste, pesticides and other forms of chemical pollution were laughed off as eco-freaks, woolly-hatted liberals or even subversive Lefties. The popular press led the vanguard in this. We macho Brits didn't care, we took in everyone else's toxins as well as our own, we sprayed our food with chemicals banned elsewhere – who cared?

Two things happened in 1988 to make people think that – perhaps – all was not well. Seals are appealing creatures and when they began dying in huge numbers at the end of the summer, attention was drawn once more to the filthy state of the North Sea. It seems that the disease is a form of canine distemper but that it affected the seals because their immune systems had been damaged by the chemical pollutants in the North Sea.

The other incident was easier to understand and that was the strange voyage of the cargo ship, the *Karin B*. For almost the first time that one can remember, big headlines appeared in the popular press over a story concerned with hazardous waste. 'Keep Out!' and 'Slam the Lid on Dustbin Britain' are typical examples.

The story of the *Karin B* began back in May 1987 when an Italian waste disposal firm began shipping consignments of highly toxic chemical waste to Nigeria where, they discovered, it could be 'disposed of', i.e. dumped, very cheaply. But the Nigerians were rapidly becoming more sophisticated about these things and, by 1988, were very worried indeed about the lethal cargoes coming into their ports. In the summer of 1988 the Nigerian government called in a firm of specialists through the offices of Friends of the Earth, whom they had approached directly on the subject.

The firm, Aspinwall & Co., duly went out to Nigeria and in June 1984 examined the lethal cocktail of chemicals which had already been dumped there by Western nations seeking a cheap option. The materials found at the dump at Koko would cost between £200 and £1,000 a tonne to dispose of by high temperature incineration in mainland Europe. In Nigeria they could be dumped for as little as £60 per load per month, paid to a local landowner. Eventually some 10,000 drums of chemicals were piled up on the site, some of which were leaking.

They contained all kinds of chemicals including the extremely toxic polychlorinated biphenyls (PCBs – the chemicals alleged to be responsible for damaging the seals' immune system), toluene, lead chromate paint waste, dichloromethane, chlorobenzene and others which were hard to analyse, being often composed of cocktails of mixed chemical waste.

The Nigerian government set about finding out who had dumped what and insisting that they removed it. The cargo which was to end up on the *Karin B* had been part of three consignments of waste probably exported by a 'waste broker', illegally imported into Nigeria by the Iruekpen Construction Co. (Nigeria) Ltd. by Gianfranco Raffaelli, an Italian national based in Nigeria.

A cargo of mixed chemicals, some in leaking drums, was loaded on to the ship (it is alleged that one man helping in the loading died whilst doing so), and set off, so it was said, for Ravenna in Italy. But the Italian people did not want their waste back. The ship's movements were being closely monitored by Friends of the Earth's toxic chemicals expert, Andrew Lees, and it is entirely due to that organization that we discovered that the waste was bound for Britain, after a somewhat circuitous voyage. The *Karin B* had sailed from Lagos on 30 July 1988, allegedly for Ravenna, but on 14 August had anchored off the Atlantic coast of Spain saying it had engine trouble.

It then transpired, only after the ship had been refused entry to the port of Neath, that the waste was bound for the Midlands' waste disposal firm, Leigh Interests of Brownhills. For once the searchlight was very firmly focused on the situation in Britain, which had allowed such a state of affairs to arise.

Waste dumping in this country has become an enormous

growth industry – and one which is government approved. The amount of hazardous waste imported into Britain has increased tenfold in the last six years, and in 1987 we imported 180,000 tonnes of toxic waste, 53,000 of which were considered to be 'special' wastes and a serious hazard. This was double the amount imported during the previous year.

The reasons are quite simple. The 'industry' has been allowed to flourish because it is a profitable one. The cost of disposing of some wastes in Britain is less than a fifth of what France and Germany charge, because our standards are lower. There is an abundance of sites in this country (about 1,500) which, together with the competitive tactics of our waste brokers and the multitude of small firms offering cut price disposal, has made us an attractive proposition for those who don't want the waste in their own backyards. Some small firms offer as little as £2 per tonne to dispose of waste in landfill sites – yet in some countries it is illegal now to dump *any* kind of chemicals in *any* kind of landfill site whatsoever.

Ten years ago local authorities were required to provide plans for dealing with wastes. Only 23 of England's 75 authorities complied and, says the Hazardous Wastes Inspectorate, wastes nowadays are 'vaguely and generally left to market forces to resolve in many of the plans that have been produced'.

Under present legislation local authorities are obliged – *by law* – to grant a licence to anyone who applies to take in toxic waste so long as the site has planning permission and can be operated without risking public health or polluting water. It does not matter if the applicant is totally unqualified, has a record of incompetence or has been found guilty previously of malpractice. His past record must not be taken into account.

The severely understaffed Hazardous Wastes Inspectorate produced three swingeingly critical reports. After the last one, its chief inspector, David Mills, resigned as no action was taken on his repeated calls for more staff and for notice to be taken of what the Inspectorate were saying. The three reports, published between 1985 and 1988 documented a truly appalling situation. They showed that no one even knows how much waste there is, that companies get rid of it in the cheapest way possible without any consideration of possible hazards, that the law is frequently

broken even by those policing it and that the situation is getting
steadily worse.

As the *Observer* reported on 4 September 1988:

> Britain's £5bn a year hazardous waste business is unique in
> Western Europe in being left almost entirely to private enterprise.
> Other countries provide public funds to ensure that high
> technology waste-disposal facilities are available.

In its 1985 report the Hazardous Wastes Inspectorate said
that the present situation gave operators 'an enviably free hand';
the following year it undertook a survey which showed that 85
per cent of site licencees broke the law by failing to make operators
record even where they put the most hazardous wastes. Only
three sites were equipped to test the content of the wastes they
received in order to discover with any certainty what they were
actually handling. What records there were showed, in some
cases, that drums of unknown waste are simply dumped in the
ground each year. Where the Inspectorate's tiny staff of five was
able to make random checks, it found that up to 40 per cent of the
chemicals dumped were unsuitable for dumping; but because it
had such a small number of inspectors, only a fraction of all the
existing sites could be examined.

The firm which was so keen to import the waste from the *Karin
B* is not one of the two considered to have adequate facilities for
incinerating PCBs (and one of these, Re-Chem, has been the
subject of endless controversy). It is based in an area where
protesting inhabitants have been complaining for years of
asthma, bronchitis, headaches and nausea. At the time the ship
was trying to offload its cargo on to them, the firm was facing a
total of sixteen charges of breaking the law, brought by Walsall
Council. The summonses had been issued in June 1988 and in
September 1988 the firm's solicitor asked that the charges be
dropped as the case had taken so long to come to court. (This
was refused and, at the time of writing, it is still pending.)

But we have been sought so eagerly as a dustbin, not only
because of our lax waste disposal rules but because of the ease
with which toxic waste can be imported. For this, we must thank
the Conservative government who, we are told, are the true

'friends of the earth'. Way back in 1983 the EEC proposed a directive on the supervision and control, within the Community, of the transfrontier shipment of hazardous waste. The British government has fought its implementation every step of the way.

However, in spite of Britain's opposition, the directive was finally agreed. It required importers of hazardous waste to provide the relevant waste disposal authority with satisfactory information on the source and composition of the waste, including the producer's identity: a detailed inventory of it and the identity of the original producers; the measures taken to ensure safe transport; and the existence of a contractual agreement with the consignee of the waste who must possess adequate technical capacity for the disposal of the waste in question 'under conditions presenting no danger to human health or the environment'.

It will be immediately apparent why Britain, with its lax controls, did not rush to implement the directive. The last date for formal compliance with it was 1 January 1987. Twenty months later, as the *Karin B* sailed towards our shores, Britain had still not implemented it. If we had implemented it and had, indeed, undertaken to do all it said – not least the formalities before it even began its journey – then the situation would never have arisen.

As it was we were still operating our own rules. Under them it was a matter for a harbourmaster, often with no knowledge or training whatsoever in the hazards of toxic waste, to decide whether to accept a ship carrying such a cargo; then responsibility was taken by the local authorities – who had all of three days to make their decision on whether or not the documentation of the cargo was accurate, and whether the waste was acceptable for 'processing' in this country, even if that 'processing' is merely a matter of dumping it into holes in the ground.

At first the government said it could do nothing as, under present law, it was up to a harbourmaster to decide whether or not to accept the ship, but finally, after the unprecedented glare of publicity across the media, the Italians were told to take their ship away and deal with it elsewhere.

We are told that the directive will now be implemented, but as late as June 1988 the government opposed a Dutch proposal to ban hazardous chemical exports from the EEC at a meeting of EEC environment ministers in Luxemburg.

The *Karin B* merely focused attention on a long-standing problem which is still with us. We just do not know how many other *Karin Bs* there may have been. It is only occasionally that instances come to light. In fact it was an earlier incident in Britain that was specially featured in the EEC directive. On that occasion a '£100 company' imported wastes from the Netherlands, stored them on a temporary site and then went into voluntary liquidation with debts of £3m, leaving its toxic chemicals to be disposed of at other people's expense.

Sir Richard Southwood, former chairman of the Royal Commission on Environmental Pollution, described the current situation as 'ramshackle and antediluvian' (*Observer*, 4 September 1988). Mr Richard Shepherd, the Conservative MP for Brownhills where Leigh Industries is situated, said 'we have the most relaxed attitude in Europe regarding waste being allowed into this country' (ibid). A top executive with an American waste disposal firm told Geoffrey Levy of the *Daily Mail* (30 August 1988) that his firm shipped waste to Britain because 'we would never be allowed to dump the stuff in the USA'.

A few more examples have leaked out. Only when it came to the salvage of the *Herald of Free Enterprise* was it discovered that she was carrying drums of toxic waste in her hold. Then, at the end of September, weeks after the furore caused by the long voyage of the *Karin B*, the *Daily Express* (not an organ noted for raising green issues) carried the headline that jumbo jets are actually flying toxic waste, including PCBs, into Britain. The newspaper discovered that an Air Canada jet, carrying 250 passengers, had brought in 27 tons of PCBs – and that they were allowed to do so under current British legislation. They were bound for the Re-Chem plant at Pontypool. Several batches of the chemical had already arrived in Britain by sea but the company transporting it fell behind schedule so asked Air Canada to take it instead. One consignment was flown in during November 1987 and two others arrived in June 1988. Air Canada told the newspaper that they were not the only airline doing it.

The Department of Trade said: 'Air Canada met every requirement so far as import licensing is concerned'. The Civil Aviation Authority said there were no regulations about using passenger planes for dangerous waste. It is just too awful to contemplate what would happen if a plane carrying PCBs crashed.

This situation was still in being when the Prime Minister made her speech, and all the time the amount of toxic waste being imported is steadily growing. Not even 'special' toxic waste appears to give any ground for concern, i.e. waste which is 'deemed to cause serious damage to an adult within 15 minutes exposure or less' – and there are now upwards of 53,000 tonnes a year of that coming in, besides the huge amount of toxic waste of a lower level.

On the same day as the Prime Minister addressed the Brighton conference, David Mills, the former chief of the Hazardous Waste Inspectorate, held a press conference. He had by now joined the environmental consultancy, Aspinwall & Co. He pointed out that the Inspectorate's three consecutive annual reports 'were all equally critical, but there was no significant improvement and no significant measures were taken'.

The government had shown no signs of finding the parliamentary time needed to enact a small batch of regulations which would improve the waste industry, many of which had been under discussion for fifteen years. These included forcing firms to demonstrate they used legal means to dispose of their waste; requiring operators of waste disposal sites to ensure the site is safe when its commercial life is over; and making it easier for waste disposal authorities to sue waste companies which break the law. Nor was there any sign that the government had any plans to give the Inspectorate the powers and resources it needed to police the situation. Mr Mills reckoned its staff needed at least to be doubled to ten.

The Inspectorate itself should also be given the powers to sue waste disposal authorities if they failed in their responsibilities. 'At the moment the Hazardous Waste Inspectorate has no teeth whatsoever', he said (*The Independent* 15 October 1988). He, and representatives of Aspinwall, stressed that it was the government's sense of political priorities which produced what they saw as a rapidly deteriorating situation which was now concerning those waste disposal firms who were responsible and who wanted tighter controls to remove the cowboy operators.

The most spectacular type of accident involving hazardous waste would be something like the crash of a jumbo jet carrying PCBs over a densely inhabited area – unlikely but not absolutely impossible. But the damage is much more likely to be insidious, caused by the leaching of chemicals into a water supply, in toxins working their way out of insecure dumps. There is already a well-documented example, that of the Love Canal housing development in the USA. Here, old waste from toxic dumps was used to infill an old canal, and a housing estate was subsequently built on the land. After a continuing history of cancers, abnormal births and miscarriages, the US government finally agreed that seepage from toxic chemicals was at the root of the problem and the families were re-housed and compensated. There is nothing at present to stop a Love Canal happening here.

Nuclear Waste

We in Britain are now sitting on a mountain of nuclear waste. We cannot say we were not warned. In 1976 the Royal Commission on Environmental Pollution chaired by the then Sir Brian, now Lord Flowers, published its sixth report, *Nuclear Power and the Environment*. On the subject of dealing with nuclear waste, it warned; 'we think that quite inadequate attention has been given to the matter and we find this is more surprising in view of the large nuclear programmes that are envisaged for the coming decades'.

The nuclear programmes were larger than the Flowers Commission knew – Mrs Thatcher stated in 1979 that she intended to see ten more nuclear power stations in ten years. That has not come to pass but the plans for more are now beginning to come to fruition.

In 1985/6 the House of Commons Select Committee on the Environment considered the question of radioactive waste in depth and expressed great concern at the lack of progress being made in Britain in safely disposing of it. They called for what they described as a 'Rolls-Royce' solution rather than the present situation, and expressed interest in the Swedish system where waste, ceaselessly monitored and properly labelled, is stored in caverns under the sea.

We have moved on little since then. Efforts by the nuclear waste disposal organisation, NIREX, to find areas where radio-active waste could be land-dumped have met with enormous opposition. They were all, as it happened, in Conservative-voting areas and immediately before the 1987 general election, it was announced that the storage plans would not, after all, go ahead. The acronym used for how people feel about having nuclear waste stored on their doorstep is NIMBY – not in my back yard!

There are three types of nuclear waste looking for a home. *Low level* – consisting of material which has become contaminated by radioactivity, e.g. gloves and overalls used in medical work, plastics, paper, building material and slightly contaminated laboratory equipment. *Intermediate level* or 'short lived' – this is more hazardous but still has only a short hazard life (or so we were told), and it does not contain plutonium. It consists of larger and more solid items, e.g. glove boxes, equipment used in work with radioactive substances, sludge from tanks, resins and odds and ends from nuclear power stations. *High level* – this consists mainly of spent fuel taken from reactors (the fuel rods themselves are taken back to Sellafield for re-processing) and any liquid waste left over from re-processing fuel rods. It is the nuclear 'waste' in the form of spent fuel rods which constitutes a hazard of its own, en route from the different power stations to Sellafield by road and rail.

There is ample documentation of what might happen if an accident occurred to a flask on its way north, or to such flasks being left unattended in venues such as railway sidings. A possible accident described by one nuclear expert posited a 10 per cent release of radioactivity from a flask travelling from the Dungeness nuclear power station when it was damaged on the railway line, while travelling through Earls Court.

> ... a west wind would force the evacuation of 80,000 people – including the Royal Family from Buckingham Palace – for twenty-five years and the loss of at least 20,000 households for

times ranging from a few months to 125 years. Even at the average cost of council housing we are talking about £400m-worth of property [at 1981 property prices!].

We are also talking about creating a ghost town in the middle of the Royal Borough of Kensington and Chelsea. A 100 per cent release would lead to the sealing off of inner London for a hundred years – and the expert used the Atomic Energy's Authority's own computer programme to make the prediction.

That is an extreme example of what might happen to nuclear waste. But all around the country the nuclear industry is having to build more and more concrete 'temporary' storage depots for it. Most of this waste is of intermediate level and it is now admitted that the definition of intermediate level waste, given earlier, is no longer quite accurate. While much of it is still of the type which will present a hazard for only a relatively short time, some is so highly irradiated that it will be potentially lethal for thousands of years and so needs to be heavily protected.

Until 1982 much of our intermediate nuclear waste was dumped in the sea – we are great sea dumpers of anything from chemicals to raw sewage. Between 1955 and 1982 some 70,000 tonnes of nuclear waste was dumped in this way until the National Union of Seamen boycotted the activity.

This means that intermediate nuclear waste has been piling up at the rate of 6,000 tonnes a year and low level at 60,000 tonnes. NIREX had proposed getting rid of this by putting the waste into trenches and said it was perfectly safe. The NIMBY objectors disagreed and, as has been said, the proposal was dropped.

So now the problem is a pressing one. The Central Electricity Generating Board (CEGB), British Nuclear Fuels at Sellafield and the United Kingdom Atomic Energy Authority are all in the process of building concrete bunkers to house waste. Friends of the Earth give the following figures for the amounts of nuclear waste waiting for a home or to go into temporary on-site concrete bunkers as at 1 January 1988.

Sellafield, 20,000 tonnes, Wylfa (Anglesey) 241 tonnes; Trawsfynfdd (North Wales) 1,785 tonnes; Hinkley Point

(Somerset) 1,850 tonnes; Berkeley (Glos.) 1,979 tonnes; Oldbury (Glos.) 421 tons; Dungeness (Kent) 420 tonnes; Aldermaston (Berks) plans for an unspecified storage capacity have been agreed; Bradwell (Essex) 760 tonnes; Sizewell (Suffolk) 900 tonnes; Heysham (Lancs) 25 tonnes; Hartlepool, 25 tonnes; Dounreay, 960 tonnes. Storage facilities are also awaited at Torness, Rosyth and Hunterston in Scotland, at Winfrith in Dorset and at Harwell in Berkshire.

In October 1988 Plymouth City Council turned down an application from the Ministry of Defence for them to be able to build a concrete nuclear waste bunker in Devonport, leaving the Navy not knowing what to do with its intermediate level nuclear waste.

By AD 2000 there will be at least 60,000 tonnes of intermediate waste in concrete bunkers across the United Kingdom.

Behind this there is an even more awful problem – what to do with the waste that will come from de-commissioned nuclear power stations. The first to be de-commissioned in this country will be Berkeley in Gloucestershire. We do not even know how to begin on this problem. As the independent nuclear consultant, John Large, told the *Observer* (16 October 1988), 'What you see here is incompetence; an industry using a new technology without being able to grasp what the end products will be. Do you know that they built the Magnox nuclear power stations with no idea of how to take them to pieces once their 25-year working life is over?'

How worrying is the problem? It was the Russian dissident scientist, Dr Zhores Medvedev, who first told the West about the nuclear waste accident at Chelyabinsk, in the Urals, some years after he had defected. He had assumed we all knew about it. It happened in 1957 but it was only in 1976, nineteen years later, that he wrote about it and was amazed at the reaction.

Sir John Hill, then chairman of the UK Atomic Energy Authority, said the story was 'rubbish' and he was joined in this view by the representatives of the nuclear industry in this country. It had long been decided that the very idea that nuclear 'waste' could actually explode was something that was not to be discussed. Then the CIA said it knew of an 'incident' at the time but that it had been caused by a faulty nuclear reactor.

Medvedev persisted in his story and was soon joined by other scientists who confirmed what he had to say, among them other defectors. Professor Lev Tumerman, former head of the biophysics laboratory at the Institute of Molecular Biology in Moscow, spoke of visiting the area and of finding a wasteland with hundreds of square miles so badly contaminated with radioactive waste that the area was uninhabitable. A doctor spoke of visiting a hospital crammed with survivors of the catastrophe, all suffering from radiation sickness. A nurse told how she became pregnant while working in the area and was advised to have an abortion.

'On both sides of the road', said Professor Tumerman, 'as far as one could see, the land was dead. No villages, no towns, only chimneys of destroyed houses, no cultivated fields or pastures, no herds, no people ... nothing. I was told this was the site of the famous Kyshtym catastrophe in which hundreds of people had been killed or disabled.'

We still do not know what caused it. If the Russians do, then, in spite of 'glasnost', they are keeping quiet about it. One theory is that a by-product of the waste reprocessing cycle, ammonium nitrate, exploded taking the waste with it. Another is that water seeped into trenches where nuclear waste was stored and triggered off a chain reaction.

America too has had its share of waste incidents, and one at the Hanford reservation in Washington State could have led to a very serious accident indeed. For a number of years there had been leakages from waste storage tanks and in 1973, when the US Atomic Energy Commission examined one of the leaks it discovered a sufficiently high level of plutonium in the soil which could, in certain circumstances, have triggered off a nuclear chain reaction.

An even more appalling situation still obtains at Canonsburg, 20 miles south of Pittsburgh, where a uranium processing facility was closed down when it was no longer needed. Its waste was then bulldozed into a swamp where radioactive sludge had been poured for years. It was covered with earth and rubble and capped with porous waste from steel mills. After a while part of the dump was used as a baseball pitch.

Hundreds of people have died of cancer in Canonsburg and it

is still an ongoing story. To give some idea of the numbers, a woman who began to check up in 1980 found 67 cases in 45 houses in one street and among the 59 people living in another, 20 had the disease. Every house in the three streets nearest to the dump had had at least one cancer or cancer-related death. The average leukaemia rate in the USA is 3.5 per 100,000. She found four cases in one street of ten houses. She also found allergies, blood problems, respiratory diseases, and tumours in the reproductive organs of young girls.

At first the authorities denied there was anything wrong but finally they were forced to act. The situation is still far from good. The waste was reclaimed and dumped on a higher site nearby, with a clay cap on it which is supposed to last from between 200 to 1000 years, or until such time as the authorities come up with a proper solution. In the meantime victims or their relatives are beginning to receive out of court settlements.

To bring the problems of nuclear waste up to date, the *Guardian* carried the following two stories on 17 October 1988.

The first detailed how the US Department of Energy had admitted the previous day that it had secretly released thousands of tonnes of radioactive uranium waste from its 37-year-old Fernald plant into the atmosphere and water supplies. In testimony before Congress, government officials acknowledged that they knew full well 'that the normal operation of the Fernald plant would result in emissions of uranium and other substances' into the Great Miami River and into the atmosphere.

The government's admission of awareness of the problem, continued the report, together with details of how much radio-active material had been emitted into the atmosphere, had been forced into the open by a lawsuit conducted by 14,000 Ohio residents against National Lead of Ohio, the contractors at the plant. It appears that some 12.7 million lbs of uranium had been disposed of in pits since the plant opened in 1951 and 167,000 lbs had been discharged into the river.

The second report concerned the notorious Sellafield (ex-Windscale) nuclear waste re-processing plant in Cumberland, which has so polluted the Irish Sea. The Labour MEP for Durham, Mr Steven Hughes, stated that a copy of a report by the French Atomic Energy Commission's Nuclear Test Centres'

Directorate, which has been available to MEPs since 25 August, says that there is now more nuclear contamination around Sellafield than at France's nuclear test site in the Pacific. Mr Hughes said he found it 'extremely alarming' that an official French document now considers their own nuclear weapons test centre is 'less contaminated than a civil nuclear power facility in a heavily populated part of the United Kingdom'.

He went on to say that either the British government has lied about contamination levels at Sellafield or the French 'have information we do not have'. The Department of the Environment has, at the time of writing, not commented.

Mr Hughes would seem to be doing a grand job but whatever criticisms might be levelled at the Thatcher administration over its foot-dragging on all aspects of environmental pollution, the record of the Labour party has been, and it still is, equally appalling on the question of nuclear waste. Its shadow Energy spokesman, John Cunningham, is as much in favour of the nuclear industry as any Conservative politician, not surprisingly as he is the member of Parliament for the area in which Sellafield is situated.

We certainly need a crash programme, lavishly funded, to find the best way of storing nuclear waste, in the light of our present knowledge – possibly a method based on the Swedish system. But, as we know that whatever happens now, we will be bequeathing an appalling problem not just to the third and fourth generation but to generations thousands of years ahead of us – a totally unknown situation – possibly we should seriously consider stopping the nuclear power programme before matters get any worse.

It would overbalance the theme of this book if one were to go into detail about the pollution of the food we eat, the air we breathe and the water we drink, let alone the worldwide issues of the 'hole in the sky', and the 'greenhouse effect'. There is a reading list at the end of the book for those who want to take it further – but these subjects deserve at least a mention, particularly as we have been told that we are in a position to lead the world in fighting for a decent environment.

Pesticides

'Pesticides to be Banned' said the headline in the *Guardian* on 2 August 1988. Pesticides based on aldrin, dieldrin and chlordane, all DDT-type pesticides, are to be phased out following an EEC directive, said the government. These pesticides are organo-chlorine based (organo-chlorines are themselves derived from nerve gas) and are among the most toxic compounds man has ever devised. They accumulate in the food chain and even Eskimo women show substantial traces of them in their breast milk.

All the media took it up and I was contacted by a TV researcher, in view of my earlier book on the subject of pesticides. The government, she said, was not actually saying they had to go now, *straight away*, but that by 1992 they should have vanished. What did I think?

This was ground I had covered some time before. Pesticides based on organo-chlorine compounds had already been banned under an earlier EEC directive as far back as 1979 (EEC Council Directive 79/117). When I found them still freely available in 1982, while researching a television programme myself, I rang the Ministry of Agriculture. I was told that they didn't have to go immediately, existing stocks could be used up, but they would have vanished by about 1985 . . .

So now, if these compounds really disappear in 1992, it will have taken thirteen years for Britain to come into line.

There are over a thousand pesticides and herbicides freely in use in Britain today. Even the herbicide 24T remains unbanned although the massive campaign against its use has meant that that use is now minimal. (245T, along with another herbicide, 24D, made up the notorious Agent Orange used in Vietnam.) We use pesticides in this country that are banned elsewhere, and also pesticides banned in the United States after it was found that false data had been used to prove them 'safe'. Every now and then the Advisory Committee on Pesticides does actually come out against a particular pesticide but it is a rare event and, as their deliberations are covered by Section 2 of the Official Secrets Act, we do not know on what basis they consider a pesticide safe or not safe.

Enormous amounts are used, often far more than the manufacturer recommends. There is what is known as 'insurance spraying' of crops, extra spraying in case it might be necessary. Some crops are sprayed anything up to ten times. Compounds contain many ingredients some of which are known to be carcinogenic or teratogenic, that is, cause birth defects. The dioxin which appears during the making of 245T (trichloro-phenoloxycetic acid) causes birth defects in animals and almost certainly has the same effect on the human foetus, as the sad pictures of grotesquely deformed babies born to Vietnamese mothers show.

According to the US National Research Council, tumours could be caused by 30 per cent of insecticides, 60 per cent of herbicides and 90 per cent of fungicides (*Report*, June 1988). The fifteen foods likely to contain highest level of residues are, in descending order of toxicity – tomatoes, beef, potatoes, oranges, lettuce, apples, peaches, pork, wheat, soya beans, other beans, carrots, chicken, corn and grapes. The NRC estimates that one in 200 cases of cancer in the USA is caused by pesticides. Other experts say it could be even more.

But proving it is very hard indeed, even proving that those who work in the agricultural industry might have been harmed by a specific pesticide or herbicide. It is possible, although even that takes far too long, to say that if most of the workers in a specific factory develop the same disease – as has happened with asbestos workers – then the common factor must be asbestos. But farm workers are, obviously, widely scattered around the country and even if a number develop a certain type of cancer and they have all used a certain spray, it is still almost impossible to prove.

This government has never concealed its opposition to statutory maximum residue limits in food and has fought hard in Europe to see that, if they are introduced, then they should be minimal. The view is that residues in Britain are 'acceptable'. Limitations on levels of sampling and analysis for residues are due mainly to financial constraints, as the London Food Commission says in its excellent report on the subject, *Pesticide Residues in Food – the Need for Real Control*. Improvements could be achieved simply by providing more resources, i.e. staff and money. Only twenty pesticides are routinely tested for, because of lack of time.

The long-term effects of low level exposure to pesticides and herbicides are extremely hard to quantify but the problem is not going to go away. The current view of the government and the agrochemical industry is that it is up to people to prove beyond all shadow of doubt that a certain pesticide is harmful to health. The sensible way would be for the agrochemical industry, supported by the government, to prove beyond a shadow of doubt that a certain pesticide is *not harmful*.

There are, however, some grounds for optimism. At the time of writing the British Medical Association has launched an investigation into the effects of pesticides on human health, and Britain will finally be forced into line by new EEC legislation to introduce maximum pesticide residues in food from January 1989 – but to test for those maximum residues will, of course, require the resources already mentioned.

Water

So to the water we drink. The massive food mountains of the EEC are a testimony to the effectiveness of the use of nitrates on the land. Nitrogen is a vital element in the environment and occurs naturally in the soil but there has been growing concern over the amount of synthetic nitrates used on land to produce big crop yields. These leach into water, either sinking down through the soil and affecting the groundwater, or running off the land into streams and rivers.

Once again this country has dragged its feet but it does seem that now, particularly as farmers are no longer to be encouraged to produce enormous surpluses, that their use of nitrates is beginning to diminish – although this will not show in the amounts found in water for some considerable time. At present, levels are still rising, particularly in areas like East Anglia and that covered by the Severn-Trent Water Authority, both high cereal-growing areas.

The effects of nitrates are complex but there is real concern that, in sufficient concentrations, they might cause stomach cancer and have an effect on the health of babies who, for obvious reasons, drink proportionately more than we do. Nitrates in water are now being linked with what is known as 'blue baby syndrome' – lack of oxygen in the baby's blood.

There is also growing proof that the amounts which leach into the North Sea are helping to produce the strange floating 'carpets' of algae now appearing, which are killing off other organisms and are hard to get rid of.

In 1980 the EEC introduced a directive on drinking water quality, which was supposed to come into force by July 1985, detailing limits for a number of residues including nitrates. The ruling covers all domestic water supplies but the government has managed to side-step the need for corrective measures by using what are described as 'derogations', which include making provision for unusual geology and permitting delays 'in exceptional cases and for a geographically defined population'. At the time of writing some 55 derogations are in use. Also, with regard to nitrates, the UK has unilaterally raised the permissible maximum level from that of the EEC limit of 50 milligrams per litre to 80 and has also defined nitrate as a non toxic substance.

One of the government's own reports published in 1987 expressed concern over substances getting into the water such as cattle slurry and silage effluent, and although polution from these sources had risen, there were fewer prosecutions, it said.

But the other major unseen pollution comes from the pesticides already mentioned. In November 1988, Friends of the Earth published results of its own investigations into pesticide pollution in water in a devastating report, *An Investigation of Pesticide Pollution in Drinking Water in England and Wales*. A survey of pesticide levels in drinking water in England and Wales, covering the period July 1985 to June 1987 revealed that the Maximum Admissible Concentration (MAC) set by the EEC for any single pesticide was exceeded in no less than 298 water sources and supplies. Breaches of the MAC for total pesticides were recorded on 76 occasions.

The detected breaches were restricted to England and specifically to the Anglian, North West, Severn-Trent, Thames, Wessex and Yorkshire regions. Friends of the Earth note, however, that the absence of reported breaches elsewhere may reflect upon inadequate investigations by water suppliers.

Each of sixteen pesticides was detected in drinking water

sources and supplies at levels above the MAC for a *single* pesticide. Those most frequently detected were Atrazine, Simazine and Mecoprop. Also alarming in view of the massive publicity given to it in the past, the herbicide 245T is still present in significant amounts. It is banned virtually everywhere else in the world except this country although here its use has fallen off dramatically because of adverse publicity.

In the manufacturing process of its base chemical, trichlorophenol oxyacetic acid, a contaminant – dioxin – appears and there can be few people now who do not know of the toxic properties of dioxin. 245T has been linked for years now to soft tissue cancers and birth defects.

Friends of the Earth contend that safety tests for the effects of pesticides in water are inadequate and data on possible effects are either lacking altogether or difficult to get. There is virtually nothing on the 'cocktail' effect – on what happens when a variety of pesticides combine together in water or how pesticides react with substances such as chlorine used in water treatment plants.

They also point out that although the MACs for pesticides in drinking water are supposed to be *legal* limits in the UK, the government, in effect, advises water suppliers to ignore them. In 1986 the Department of the Environment recommended to them that instead they should rely on the 'guideline values' for pesticides in drinking water published in 1984 by the World Health Organization or, where no such values existed, the government's own 'guide concentrations' based upon advice from the Department of Health.

With the appearance of the Water Bill to privatize water in the 1988 Queen's Speech, government spokesmen have been describing the MACs as 'out of date' and stating that other governments agree with Britain's views on pesticide levels in water. Only Italy appears to do so and Italy too continues to breach the EEC directive.

Perhaps the measure of government commitment to 'green issues' can be estimated by the fact that instead of taking action to ensure that drinking water complies with the MACs for pesticides, it is pressing the EEC to draft an amendment to the drinking water directive which replaces the MACs with limits for individual pesticides 'which are more closely related to health-risks', presumably even if they do not even know what these are.

This whole issue is one that will be thrown into the balance when water is privatized and profits to shareholders take priority over everything else. We can none of us avoid the consequences of what happens to our water – it is essential to life. Nor – as will be shown in the Epilogue – what happens if, accidentally, such a supply is actually poisoned.

The Ozone Layer

It was back in 1974 that rumours began to circulate in scientific circles that something was going badly wrong with the ozone layer. Ozone is a gas made up of three oxygen molecules and varies considerably in thickness. It is at its densest between 10 and 30 kilometres above the earth but it is still a thin layer. However this seemingly thin and unimportant layer of gases soaks up ultraviolet rays from the sun and stops potentially lethal levels of radiation from reaching the earth. Gradually it became apparent that a large hole was appearing in the ozone layer over Antarctica. By mid-1987 it had assumed gigantic proportions and was the size of the USA. (In 1988 it appears to have lessened in size.)

Many scientists became convinced it was caused in part by the increasing use of chlorofluorocarbons, or CFCs. CFCs are used as a propellant in many aerosols and in the manufacture of polystyrene foam. So why should this worry us, you might say.

But the solar ultraviolet radiation which is filtered out could cause severe damage to human beings, not least skin cancer, and the effect from a large hole would be a skin cancer epidemic. American scientists estimate that even a small increase in ultraviolet rays could cause a million extra cancers over the lifetime of the current population, 20,000 of which would end in death. Other nasty effects include eye disease, such as cataracts, and even dramatic and irreversible changes in weather patterns as man-made chemicals interact with natural ones.

Gradually, country after country, led by the USA, began to press for a drastic reduction in the use of CFCs. Mrs Thatcher, in her environment speech, paid special attention to the ozone layer and action taken by Britain. The reality is slightly different. When, in September 1987 the USA called for a reduction in their use of 80 per cent, Britain alone opposed it. In fact it was British officials who had nearly scuttled the previous effort at agreement back in 1986. In the spring of 1987 the Department of the Environment was *still* insisting that the damage to the ozone layer and subsequent threat to health was trumped up by politically motivated and/or hysterical pressure groups such as Friends of the Earth and Greenpeace.

In August 1986 the government had claimed – basing its information on an official report – that there was nothing to worry about and had therefore continued fighting to ensure that if there were to be any controls, they should be minimal. So there was no little embarrassment when two of the authors of the report so confidently quoted, Dr Joe Farman, director of the British Antarctic Survey (who first discovered the ozone hole) and Dr John Pyle of Cambridge University, publicly dissociated themselves from the government's use of their report. It was, they said, already out of date and drastic action was necessary.

Meanwhile in her speech, Mrs Thatcher had praised the 'world lead' achieved in Britain in the discovery of, and then research into, the hole in the ozone layer. This again prompted Dr Joe Farman into print. In a report in the *New Scientist* (8 October 1988), he said that Britain had, in fact, 'squandered' its 'world lead'. He blamed poor funding for giving a 'fragmented and uncoordinated' approach to the work. He concluded:

> Although great play continues to be made of the discovery of the Antarctic ozone hole by British Antarctic Survey scientists, the potential for subsequent basic and strategic research in the UK has not been realised. Indeed, the promotion and proper resourcing of fundamental research in this area of major concern has been quite inadequate. The major scientific initiatives since 1985 have been taken elsewhere – notably in the USA.

At the time of writing Britain is, reluctantly, coming into line with the rest of Europe on the amount of CFCs it will permit to be released into the atmosphere.

It is not possible to rehearse the whole list of issues here on which the British government has at best dragged its feet and at worst opposed ameliorative measures with every means in its power. This has applied to acid rain (we are still trying to hold things up to avoid having to alter our policies), the promotion of lead-free petrol, the dumping of toxic waste and sewage in the North Sea and cleaning up our beaches to standards considered acceptable to the EEC.

On the question of dumping sewage, Environment Minister Nicholas Ridley told the House of Commons in November 1988 that 'experts' had told him it was perfectly safe and acceptable in spite of what the EEC had to say about it. He was promptly taken to task by the Conservative MP Richard Body, who had chaired a Select Committee on the subject and had taken opinions from scientific experts who had come to a totally different conclusion.

Then there is the 'greenhouse effect' caused by the heating up of the earth's atmosphere, thought to be due to pollution from, among other things, fossil fuel power stations and exhaust gases from cars. (We are now told by some scientists that the effects of this heating up will show themselves as soon as the 1990s.)

The 'greenhouse effect' on the Prime Minister has been an illuminating one because it appears to have had a considerable influence on her apparent conversion to green politics as she has been able to combine concern over it with her committed support of nuclear power. Nuclear power, she says emphatically, will save us from the greenhouse effect.

The answer to this has been put so cogently in a letter to *The Independent* from Dr P. M. Kelly of the Climate Research Unit of the University of East Anglia on 3 November 1988, that it is worth quoting almost in full. He writes:

> The greenhouse effect represents a serious threat to humanity's welfare and it saddens me to see the issue being manipulated in a short-sighted and cynical fashion by those who advocate expansion of the nuclear programme. Perhaps I can provide the answer to the question that Nicholas Ridley was unable – or unwilling – to answer on BBC's *On the Record* as reported in *The Independent* (31 October 1988). How many nuclear power stations would be needed to limit the rise in carbon dioxide levels?

Researchers at the Rocky Mountain Institute in the United States have demonstrated that to produce a substantial reduction in global carbon dioxide emissions over the next forty years through nuclear substitution would require the commissioning of 'one 1000MW nuclear power station at some point on the planet *every one to four days*' [my italics]. The cost would be astronomical, of the order of £500bn per year, requiring a colossal increase in rates of economic growth.

The UK would have to bring at least three and perhaps ten nuclear power stations on line each year to reduce its emissions of carbon dioxide – neither a practicable nor a palatable proposition.

Funds would be diverted away from improving energy efficiency and conservation, effectively increasing the emissions the nuclear strategy attempts to reduce. Pound for pound, investment in improving energy efficiency and in conservation measures would prove a factor up to ten times more effective as a means of reducing carbon dioxide emissions.

There is no need to choose between the nuclear option and global warming. Improving energy efficiency attacks the root cause of the greenhouse problem and would have a wide range of environmental and economic benefits. To advocate a leap out of the coal-fired frying pan into the nuclear fire without consideration of the wider environmental and economic implications of such a policy suggests that the new recruits to the environmentalist movement still have much homework to do.

It could not be put better than that.

But the sub-text to the drum-banging of the new environmentalists is more ominous. Nicholas Ridley said quite bluntly at the Conservative conference in 1988 that if people wanted to clean up the environment and have less pollution, then it is they who will have to pay for it, not those who cause the pollution.

The pollution of the world in general, and the British Isles in particular, is indeed a slow burning fuse and there is unlikely to be a single specific catastrophe which will bring it to the forefront of public concern, although it is not impossible. However there are heartening signs that more people here are becoming worried – although not to the extent of those living in the United States where the environment has become a top issue.

It is encouraging to see that the present government has, finally, recognized that there is now concern about pollution but speeches which are not backed up by effective and meaningful action are irrelevant to the issues facing us today. Words come cheap.

It is relatively easy, although even here there needs to be positive action, to modify a Ro-Ro ferry so that it will not capsize and to employ sufficient cleaning and maintenance staff to ensure that dirty, greasy rubbish does not build up near escalators on the London Underground. It requires more long-term planning to clean up our environment but the kind of damage we are doing to it, which can cause sickness and widespread permanent changes, cannot be rectified afterwards. It has to be tackled now.

If you are rich and privileged you can, by buying your way, avoid having to face many hazards. You can travel in a chauffeur-driven car and never risk yourself on dirty, overcrowded, unsafe public transport. If you are in the government you can fly in military aircraft and ensure, so far as is possible, that your airspace is safe. You will not make cheap trips to the continent on Ro-Ro ferries. You can buy private medicine and private schooling, ensure you have a fine home in a decent environment that is not situated in a back street next to an unmarked chemical waste dump.

But you cannot insulate yourself from the effects of the pollution of the planet. Acid rain falls on you just as it does on everyone else; you cannot guarantee that you will never drink polluted water; and, as for the hole in the ozone layer, the dangerous rays from the sun will hit you, your children and your grandchildren with a fine lack of selectivity.

There has been ample warning of all the hazards mentioned in this chapter – more than enough of it one would imagine. As Dr Robin Russell Jones, an expert on pollution, says however:

> The attitude of this government to all types of pollution makes me despair. Consumers are now the only people who have it within their power to influence what happens by bringing real financial pressure to bear and that, unfortunately, seems to be the only way nowadays of bringing about change.

Speaking of the hole in the ozone layer he expressed his hope that in future the government, and everyone else, would

pay a little more attention to the scientists when they correctly predict the environmental consequences of uncontrolled industrial releases. Chernobyl was bad enough but to hazard the integrity of the global environment for hamburger cartons and spray-on deodorants seems criminally irresponsible.

The Prime Minister in Brighton in 1988 described her party as the 'stewards of the earth'. Just look at the record.

10 Can We Learn from Experience?

Send not to know for whom the bell tolls,
It tolls for thee.

John Donne

Nobody can guarantee that they will not die prematurely or be maimed in an accident. You could stay in bed all your life only to have the ceiling fall down on you. You can become a casualty merely by crossing the road at the wrong time. Statistically, you are far more likely to be killed in a car crash on our congested roads than in a mid-air collision over Gatwick; or to die of cancer as a result of smoking cigarettes than you are by living close to a nuclear power plant.

That is all quite true but all those factors obtained equally for those people who happily set off on a day trip to Zeebrugge and back, those who left their offices and made their way home to their friends and families via King's Cross, or those who boarded the DC10. Yet they all provided the unpleasant kind of statistic.

As was said at the beginning of the book it is impossible to guarantee that every kind of disaster can be prophesied in advance and thereby avoided, given sufficient energy and forethought, enough cash and enough sense of self-preservation. The unfortunate inhabitants of Pompeii could do little about the fate from Vesuvius which was literally hanging over them nor could those who drowned in the Flood unless, like Noah, they had a hot line to God.

But the disasters past and possibly to come, which have been examined here, could and should be avoided. No recent government has a clean record on disaster prevention and virtually all large organizations have been prepared to take risks and cut corners rather than make safety an absolute priority. When a hazard is less immediate, like the dangers from working with asbestos, pesticide residues in food, harm from low level radiation or seepage from toxic waste – then, more often than not, those responsible can get by on crossing their fingers and hoping that when the balloon goes up they will no longer be around to take the blame.

But I do not believe that it is fortuitous that we have had three major disasters in so short a period under the Thatcher administration. This government has made an idol of profit. What is not profitable is worthless in every sense of the word. Alongside this belief goes another – all state or nationalized industries and services are bad, all privatized industries and utilities are good – gas, electricity, oil, all forms of transport, even water, have been or are to be sold off for quick cash returns.

There is a direct link between profitability and Zeebrugge, King's Cross and Piper Alpha. Those industries originally in private hands or already privatized must put their profits to shareholders first. Those industries waiting to be privatized, like London Transport, must be made economic and fattened up ready for sale so that sufficient funds can be attracted when sale day comes.

The wreck of the *Herald of Free Enterprise* was, in part, brought about by three individuals but was overwhelmingly the result of the 'sloppy management' described at the inquiry, and the cost cutting that had put profit first. The continual overloading of the ferries against every rule of the sea was overlooked because it meant more money taken in fares. It became the norm, not the exception, to clip over a quarter of an hour off the turnaround time to keep profits up. Who knows, had the ship been turned around in the time properly allowed for the job then it might well be that there would have been ample time to check the bow doors.

The King's Cross fire should not have come as a surprise to anybody. There had, as has been shown, been countless fires on the underground and the Fire Inspections had routinely reported the build-up of rubbish, dirt and grease. But staff and maintenance had been cut back to the bone because London Transport's Underground section had to be made profitable.

Already subsidized less than any comparable system in the world, it must learn to pay its own way.

The results of the Piper Alpha inquiry have still to be published but it is obvious that there had been very real worries and warnings for a considerable time before the disaster about the state of the rig and that, in general, there had been substantial cutbacks in maintenance as the price of oil continued to fall.

The general climate of the times was blamed in robust fashion by Frank Dobson, MP as he looked at the burned out King's Cross booking hall in his own constituency.

> Clearly London Underground gave safety a low priority. But they were only taking their lead from a government which gives safety a low priority and which in transport, as in other spheres, confuses cost-cutting with efficiency.
>
> But this attitude is not only self-serving, it's also short-sighted. Because everyone is at risk from highly flammable aircraft seats installed because safer ones cost a bit more; and ferries whose scheduled sailing times required them to leave port overladen and unsafe; and a Prime Minister who demands staff cuts in the emergency services and then turns up at tragedies to pay televised tributes to the firefighters, ambulance and hospital staff who have struggled yet again to do their magnificent best. If this is what Mrs Thatcher means by the values of an enterprise culture then, as far as I'm concerned, she can stuff it.

But even if Mr Dobson and all who think like him are quite, quite wrong then can we learn from past experience? The answer is, quite definitely, yes, we can.

Ro-Ro Ferries

It was apparently beyond the wit of the ferry companies to discover how much it would cost to put in the transverse bulkheads which the inquiry judge and a host of professional naval experts consider would make these vessels safer, so Granada Television, took the initiative and kindly commissioned a firm of experts to do it for them. As we have seen, passengers polled on that programme were prepared to pay pounds, not just pence, to prevent a re-run of Zeebrugge – which would be necessary only if the entire cost was passed on. This safety measure should be put in hand at once. No amount of PR will allow ferry company management to survive another Ro-Ro ferry disaster in British waters.

The London Underground

As is apparent to all those who use the system it is still quite, quite *awful* – congested, dirty, lacking in staff, with escalators and lifts endlessly out of order. (From April to June 1988 one out of four lifts and one out of six escalators were out of order at any one time.)

Obviously the Fennell recommendations must be implemented but there needs to be more than that. There should be a full and comprehensive safety audit now and another in twelve months to ensure that what was needed to be done has, in fact, been done. Fire certification *must* be brought in – while this long, slow deliberation is going on as to what the law does or does not mean we could have another fatal fire. Ms Snell and London Transport should have to spend the £110m put away in case they were forced to bring standards up to scratch. They must at the very least reach a level at which fire certification would be granted.

A basic minimum of maintenance staff per station should be set to ensure that stations really are kept clean and free from fire hazards: the most recent London Fire Brigade report shows that this is still not the case.

One-man-operated trains should also be looked at. It might sound like a splendid saving to do away with the guard but there has already been one documented instance of a driver being unaware that the back of his train was smouldering until he reached a platform, (which was, as we have seen, empty of staff). The number of guards on London Underground has been cut by 23 per cent since 1983 and, as one of the King's Cross survivors put it, 'What does LRT management think the word "guard" means, for Heaven's sake?'

The new ticketing system will mean that a further 1500 staff will go over the next few years but where does that leave the workings of the new automatic gates? At one stage it was proposed to erect huge cages on top of the four-foot barriers. Have these been adequately tested for safety? Should there be a complete re-think following King's Cross? What would have happened had they been in place on that fatal night? There are no answers to these questions at present from London Transport.

It should be proved publicly and without a shadow of doubt that, in the event of a real emergency, the new gates would not prove a hazard to the public. It is interesting to note how few people use them, preferring to squash through the opening where there is a ticket collector.

Not only should there be training for staff in fire drills, we should also copy the Paris Metro and have fire drills involving the public too – however inconvenient and unpopular these might be. It might be your life you save later by taking part in one now.

The Oil Industry

The Secretary of State for energy has finally made the first step in allowing Safety Committees to be set up on rigs. He is still refusing to allow the men who work on the rigs to be represented on them. This is not good enough. It is not he, nor the senior management of oil companies, nor the shareholders who are at risk. It is the men who work on the rigs and they know better than anyone else if there is a problem. So they should have representation.

This would also mean that men who are worried about some safety angle could go to their own representative and have the matter taken up without fearing they will lose their employment as a result. If no union representation on Safety Committees is allowed, then it is even more urgent that some way is found to allow those who have seen a hazard to be able to report it, not to suffer by so doing. It must also be seen to be acted upon.

It would seem too that there needs to be a review of safety procedures in the light of the fact that the men on Piper Alpha did all they had been trained to do, yet died because they waited too long to be told to evacuate the rig.

Lastly, and most important, the health and safety aspect of work on the rigs must be separated from the Department of Energy, whose priority is revenue, and handed over to the Department of Trade which is not so directly involved.

How about those disasters possibly in the pipeline? Measures could be taken now to try and avoid these ever taking place.

Avoiding a Mid-Air Collision

Well, there is to be a new computer at Air Traffic Control and that must be an improvement. But more is needed than that. It is patently absurd that only near misses reported by pilots are logged by the Civil Aviation Authority. Those observed by Air Traffic Controllers must be logged too to give a true picture. There needs to be a sufficient number of Air Traffic Controllers and the number of hours they work should have a legal limit. However much they might want to make a profit, the British Airports Authority should not be allowed to opt out of the national air traffic control system at West Drayton. Free market forces cannot rule the air. Deregulation without restraint or check cannot possibly prove to be a safer system. The government should think again and be pressed to do so by those who use the air. Only an idiot would be prepared to take a cut-price flight and hang safety.

Pilot Fatigue

We are at risk of talking about this and discussing it until the great disaster occurs. There is now ample evidence that this is still a growing problem. Whatever the reasons behind the suppression of the 1973 BALPA Report, its message was clear – that pilot fatigue had become the major current threat to air safety. There needs to be another investigation and report into the subject and it does not need to take years to research and yet more years before publication. It needs to be undertaken quickly and any recommendations acted upon. If a forthcoming big air disaster is thought to have been caused by pilot fatigue, then no airline will be able to excuse itself by saying that it was not aware that there was any problem.

Pilotage

At the end of the first year without a Trinity House pilotage service, there should be a detailed survey into how the new system has worked. Account should be taken of any near collisions reported by vessels or any problems they have encountered. The pilots themselves should be asked how the new system is working out, and the ports must report on the pilotage system they are using and its cost. Otherwise we will have to wait for an accident to happen before all this takes place.

The Channel Tunnel

Nobody should now be in any doubt, having read papers by so many experts on fire safety and tunnel hazards, that regardless of how it might affect profit, it would be little less than insane to put people inside their cars and lorries to transport them through the Channel Tunnel. There are just too many possibilities of error. It is not too late for the decision to be taken that cars, lorries and caravans *must* travel quite separately from people.

Nuclear Power

Finance should be made available immediately to fund sufficient inspectors to inspect all those nuclear power plants which are behind schedule on their safety inspection. If there are any doubts at all about any of them continuing safely, then they should be closed down immediately, like Berkeley. Preferably nuclear power should be phased out – a truly energetic programme of energy conservation would make this expensive method of producing electricity unnecessary.

Pollution

Toxic Waste

Given a true political will we could, at least, prevent there being even more damage to our environment. There should be strict new rules on the dumping of toxic waste and sufficient inspectors employed to ensure that all existing dumps can be properly monitored. There should be huge fines and, if necessary, prison sentences, for those who break the law. If we want to show our expertise in dealing with toxic waste, then let us export that expertise to other countries and show them how to do it, rather than take in everyone else's toxic rubbish.

Nuclear Waste

The House of Commons Select Committee on this subject made a number of sensible recommendations which should be acted upon. Nobody has really cracked this problem yet but the next best thing is, as the Select Committee suggested, the 'Rolls-Royce solution', possibly on the lines of that operated in Sweden.

Pesticides

When a pesticide is 'banned', it should mean just that. The Advisory Committee on Pesticides should not sit in secret nor should its deliberations be covered by the Official Secrets Act. It should openly make known how it arrived at its conclusion that a certain pesticide was safe. There should be a review of the numbers of pesticides flooding into the market. A properly funded survey should be undertaken of all those who claim to have been affected by pesticide poisoning – all past surveys have been undertaken on a shoestring and this is just not good enough. Above all it should be mandatory that a chemical firm prove beyond all shadow of doubt that a pesticide is safe if properly used, and not be left to the unfortunate consumer to try and prove that it was not.

The Environment

A massive programme of energy conservation would go a long way to help solve some of the most pressing problems, as Dr Kelly explained in his letter to *The Independent*. It would help deal with the questions of nuclear power, acid rain and the greenhouse effect. All the warnings, now swelling into a massive chorus of experts openly describing the situation as 'catastrophic', will come to nothing but words unless there is sufficient public pressure to force change.

A long hard look also needs to be taken into how we deal with the aftermath of accidents. It had not escaped notice that, prior to the publication of the King's Cross report, it was the small people who had carried the can and suffered. People still remember the illiterate Turkish baggage handlers, who left the cargo door open on the DC10 back in 1975 which brought about the subsequent disaster. Few bothered to look at the small print of the subsequent inquiry and read the history of unheeded warnings and recommendations.

The sleepy young assistant bosun and the arguments over the responsibility of the master of the *Herald of Free Enterprise* still go on and there is absolutely no sign, unless the Kent Police finally act, or the families succeed in getting a case into court, that heads at the top will roll. While Sir Keith Bright and Dr Tony Ridley, belatedly, did the right thing and resigned, there is nothing to lead us to believe that the head of P & O, Sir Jeffrey Sterling, is likely to do the same.

Speaking on television on 9 October 1987 he said: 'To suggest that they [the directors of the ferry company] had a direct effect on the ferry capsizing in my view would be totally wrong . . . I think it gets a bit far fetched that somebody sitting on shore should be hauled up in a similar context [to the captain, chief officer and assistant bosun].'

What is needed is a test case on corporate responsibility. It is worrying, therefore, to learn of the direct intervention of the Lord Chief Justice in the King's Cross inquest. This was well put in a letter from Celia Wells, a lecturer at Cardiff Law School, to the *Guardian* (14 October 1988). She writes:

In your Comment column on the King's Cross Inquest you supported the coroner's view that his court should not be used as a forum for determining civil and criminal liability. Both you, and he, seemed to be fortified or influenced by the advice of the Lord Chief Justice.

What was the nature of that advice, I wonder; a little note pushed under the door? I was not aware that the Lord Chief Justice had the right to dictate to judges the proper jurisdiction of their courts.

Be that as it may, it is inaccurate to portray the role of the coroner's court as unconcerned with criminal liability. An inquest does not determine who was responsible but the range of verdicts does allow the jury to give its opinion as to whether death was caused accidentally or unlawfully.

You also suggest that the Zeebrugge inquest jury defied a direction not to return verdicts of unlawful killing. What the coroner there said was that the jury could only base an unlawful death finding on the acts of individuals, not of corporate negligence.

She adds that she does agree with the 'Commentary' writer's conclusion that 'corporate liability for manslaughter is in urgent need of testing in relation to these tragedies'. She also wonders just what will happen if the relatives in all the outstanding cases bring private prosecutions as threatened. 'It will be interesting to see if the Director of Public Prosecutions will invoke his right to take them over and offer no evidence' – in other words ensure that there is no test in the courts.

The rights of the bereaved were further taken up by *The Independent* in its leader following the publication of the Fennell Report which concluded: 'It remains for victims' relatives to decide whether there is enough evidence for a private prosecution of those at the top for corporate manslaughter. Until such a prosecution takes place, inefficient managers in a hostile environment are unlikely to treat safety with sufficient seriousness' – which is a horrifying thought.

Corporate responsibility can be used in other countries, so why not here? At present prosecutions on the grounds of public safety are a relative formality and the fines minimal. In these circumstances it is not surprising that many organizations can afford to gamble with safety and feel they can cope with any consequent legal action. As *The Independent* points out it may well take the first major disaster involving public fatalities which is followed by the first corporate manslaughter charge, to change the situation.

As we have seen when a disaster does occur then the rescue services respond magnificently; but recently there have been growing calls for some kind of national disaster relief service, although opinions are divided as to how best this should be organized.

In the aftermath of Piper Alpha one of the senior consultants involved in treating the victims, plastic surgeon Mr Colin Rayner of Aberdeen Royal Infirmary, spoke of how his task and that of his colleagues had been made easier by a totally fortuitous set of circumstances. At the time of the disaster the country's leading burns specialists were attending a conference in Leicester, and he and others left immediately for Aberdeen once the scale of the task became known. This enabled Mr Rayner to form three surgical teams with up to six specialists in each.

'I really believe we would have had difficulty', he told the *Guardian* (14 July 1988), if it had not been for the Leicester conference. With our normal staff we would still have been working to do what was necessary in the first instance.

'Instead we were able to undertake the initial work in the first 72 hours. You try and operate on people within the first four days if possible because infection comes after that – do it within that time scale and you can save them weeks in hospital.'

Mr Rayner believes that professional organizations within the health service should advise on the setting up of a co-ordinated system of specialists in aid as part of an overall nationwide disaster plan. There would also need to be a stockpile of specialist equipment.

As was noted in the chapter on nuclear power, present disaster arrangements are haphazard and some areas do not seem to have any at all. He felt that where there was a need for a speciality like his, which was in short supply (there are only 112 plastic surgeons in Britain), they need to be able to be nationally co-ordinated.

The predictable response of the government hitherto is that no national disaster plan is necessary. In the wake of Piper Alpha, Junior Home Office Minister, Lord Ferrers, said he thought it was sufficient that responsibility for disaster organization should rest with local and regional co-ordinators. However, since the Fennell Report the government appears prepared to think again.

The need for such planning is widely recognized abroad. In the United States there is, certainly, state and local level emergency disaster planning but there is also an emergency management agency which is part of the national government. This provides the state and local authorities with help and advice on planning for the prevention of, as well as coping with, disasters. It also co-ordinates federal aid when the president declares an emergency or major disaster, when the situation is too severe to be dealt with adequately by local and state efforts alone, and it administers the federal emergency plan.

In France all regional authorities have – by law – to prepare general plans for coping with major emergencies. As well as this there is also a national centre which stores useful and necessary information and which can provide help to any local area when it is needed.

In Australia, as in the USA, disaster planning is mainly the responsibility of the states but there is also, at national level, a National Disasters Organization (NDO). This organization develops the Australian Disaster Plan which covers more than just natural disasters like forest fires and operates a National Emergency Operations Centre. It also provides assistance to any state which requires it.

There are obvious models for serious consideration here. What is lacking is any sense of urgency or the will to consider them; and here we come to one of the most worrying aspects of the whole subject and that is public apathy and lack of public interest.

There is obviously no easy answer. A triumphalist government in its third term and still with a huge majority can afford, much of the time, to take little notice of its critics or even of views other than its own. Such a situation leads to apathy and even despair among those who want to see something put right.

But there is more to it even than that. A major disaster does, for a little while, affect us all. The public always responds generously with donations of cash. They tell each other how awful it must have been and then memories fade very quickly. So much on television is given equal weight and time – a Royal visit, unemployment figures, a jolly tale about a zoo, a bereaved family. For a few hours or days a national disaster will receive above average time but then it slips back into the usual round of news. Starving people in a famine in the Sudan give place to cash quiz shows and minds are wiped of the images. There are chilling conclusions to be drawn from this when the television networks go out to the highest bidders with the biggest cash bid as the only criterion.

Television now seems to be the last refuge of the investigative journalist with items such as James Cutler's programmes on nuclear power for Yorkshire Television, Granada's *World in Action* and BBC2's *Brass Tacks*. Will they go the way of investigative journalism in the newspapers?

After a few human interest stories following a disaster, sometimes of a blatantly intrusive kind, the popular papers revert to their usual diet of the love lives of soap opera stars, the drunken habits of football hooligans, all the fun of the fair, which makes our popular media the laughing stock of Europe – and, apart from *The Independent*, the *Observer*, and the *Guardian*, and now only marginally, the *Daily Mirror*, there is no view other than that of the current administration. It is peddled uncritically both directly and subtly and there is no longer space for dissent.

'There is no such thing as society', said the Prime Minister and more and more it is going that way. Young people walk around cut off from anything by their Sony Walkmen; the sheer problems of survival in the enterprise culture, trying to find a home and keep it, keeping a job when unemployment is still high and real jobs hard to get, making ends meet if you are unfortunate enough not to be part of the economic 'miracle', all lead to inturned and self-absorbed behaviour. Older people wring their hands in despair and turn their backs on it.

Yet without public pressure there will be more disasters and they will occur at ever shortening intervals and it is only public pressure that can prevent them.

Only a raving idiot would put cost cutting before his or her personal safety. Do you really want to take a chance on another ferry capsizing, or getting caught in another London Underground fire for the sake of a few pence? Would you really prefer to jet off on holiday on an aircraft owned by some cowboy airline into totally de-regulated skies rather than pay a few pounds more and have the assurance that the number of aircraft up there are regulated and that you will, so far as is humanly possible, arrive at your destination alive? Will you have sleepless nights over the shareholders of Eurotunnel if their return on investment is smaller because safety has had to be put first?

Every time members of the public are actually asked about this, following the latest catastrophe, they *always* say they think safety should be the first priority.

There are some small actions that anyone can take. You can write to the ferry companies asking what they propose to do about installing transverse bulkheads in Ro-Ro ferries since so many experts consider this necessary and it has been shown that the cost is relatively modest. You can inform them that you personally will be travelling in future only with the ferry company that does this.

You can write to London Underground every time you stumble over piles of litter or see an obvious fire hazard and also to the London weekly paper and the *Standard* about what you have seen.

If you do not like the idea of a free-for-all in the air when you go on holiday in 1992, then tell Lord Brabazon what you think, c/o the House of Lords. Ask him to explain exactly how and why free market forces will make our airspace a better and safer place; and tell him you will note his reply and keep it by you in case his optimism is not borne out. Do not be afraid to do this – it is more likely to be your name on the coffin in the event of a mid-air collision in de-regulated air space, than it is his.

Likewise, if you do not fancy frying in your car because someone in front of you has lit up a cigarette in the depths of the Channel Tunnel, tell the Eurotunnel consortium while they are still building it. Large numbers of potential customers publicly threatening to boycott the Tunnel unless people are separated from vehicles might, even at this late stage, make them change their minds.

And on all these issues and the environmental ones too, there is still your MP. Even if you consider him or her merely lobby fodder, you can still make him or her aware of your concerns and a sufficient number of concerned letters can have an effect even in the current Parliament. As has been shown with issues like freezing Child Benefit and charges for eye and dental tests, it is even possible on occasion to get some of the worms to turn.

For it is a sure and certain thing that all around you there are Ministers, MPs, company chairmen, company press officers and PR consultants who will be wheeled out to gloss over the next disaster.

As the first news comes in, the toiling scribe will be at his typewriter or word processor working away on the press release – 'could not have been foreseen', 'totally unexpected', 'no warning', 'every care taken with public safety', 'a freak wave', 'dense fog', 'an unprecedented flash fire', 'safest airspace in the world', 'no reason to believe . . . ', etc., etc.

If you are lucky, you will be listening to what he has to say. If you are not lucky, you will know nothing about it. Anyone – you, me, the children, Uncle George – *anyone* can be a statistic in a disaster.

John Donne put it better than anyone. After noting that 'any man's death diminishes me, because I am involv'd in Mankind', he ended his homily with:

> Send not to know for whom the bell tolls,
> It tolls for thee.

Epilogue: A Trust Betrayed

> I think one could look on this as a major ecological disaster the like of which has not been recorded in Britain before.
> *Dr Neil Ward Doctor of Chemistry at the University of Surrey*

This story is put last because it is a microcosm of all that has gone before. It did not make the national headlines although it was mentioned in the national press. Nobody has died. Yet. The long-term effects of what happened have yet to show up. While the stories of the *Herald of Free Enterprise*, the King's Cross fire and Piper Alpha hit the headlines and public inquiries were set up, information about what happened in North Cornwall in the summer of 1988 has only trickled out.

It was an accident which – according to 'Hazard' studies of the kind used to tell us whether or not chemical accidents, or indeed nuclear ones, are possible – could not happen; but it did happen. All the ingredients for it were there.

On 6 July 1988 a tanker driver arrived at the Lowermoor water treatment works in the Fowey district of the South West Water Authority (SWWA). The works are largely automatic and for much of the time unmanned. The driver was a relief driver for a chemical firm, unfamiliar with the layout of the works. He was carrying a load of aluminium sulphate, an agent used by the water industry. The firm which supplied the chemical did not label it as a hazardous substance. That was the first ingredient.

The relief driver, who had only received an oral briefing, had been given a key by one of the regular drivers. The key fitted any of the tanks in the waterworks. It should have been foreseen that an accident might be possible given this circumstance, but it was not. That was the second ingredient.

When the driver arrived, there was nobody at Lowermoor. He found what he thought was the correct tank, unlocked it and dumped his load of aluminium sulphate into it. He then pushed an unsigned delivery note under the office door. It had not been thought necessary to supervise the delivery. That was the third ingredient.

The driver had not put his load into the correct tank. He had dumped it into a tank of purified water on its way to the mains supply and this was to affect 7,000 households and 20,000 people in the Camelford area.

The results were immediate as the twenty tons of aluminium sulphate hit the mains supply. The water was badly discoloured and a number of people rang South West Water to find out why, but they were told there was nothing wrong. They drank it and 20,000 people developed a wide and extremely nasty range of symptoms. Some could almost be called comic – women whose hair had been tinted or bleached found that it went green. Other symptoms were certainly not comic – people developed sickness, diarrhoea, mouth and nose ulcers, blood in their urine, various aches and pains and those already suffering from arthritis found themselves in excruciating agony.

What followed was one of the most extraordinary cover ups of recent years.

Acidity and alkalinity in water are measured on a continuous scale by a property known as 'pH'. Acids have a low pH and alkalis a high one. It is measured on a scale of 1–14 and a good water supply should average out at around 7. Aluminium sulphate is an acid.

When the first calls began to come into South West Water, they came at a time when two minor accidents had already occurred on that same day. A blockage had been found in the pre-lime dosing pump and this was put right about 8.30 a.m. There was more trouble at 6 p.m. and again it was put right. The inadequately briefed driver of the load of aluminium sulphate had arrived in between the two incidents at about 4.30 p.m.

It was clear that, for hours, officials at South West Water flatly refused to believe there was a problem. A mother, who rang and asked if the water was safe to make up a bottle for her baby, was told it was. She did so and the baby developed mouth ulcers.

The local GP, Doctor Richard Newman, found his surgery flooded with patients exhibiting a range of distressing symptoms. South West Water kept silent.

The day after the dumping, on 7 July 1988, 30,000 fish were found dead in the Camel and Allen rivers. South West Water blamed an equipment failure.

On 11 July, Douglas Cross, a biologist and expert on water pollution who actually lives in the Camelford area, complained of kidney pains and contacted South West Water. His complaint was rejected. Only afterwards did it come out that South West Water had at last become fully aware of the delivery of aluminium sulphate to the wrong tank three days earlier on 8 July. Meanwhile stories were getting into the local media of illness in the Camelford area and of something being wrong with the water.

At this stage – when the full implications of the disaster had become clear – South West Water should have alerted everybody, the general public, the media, the district health authority, and provided an alternative water supply. Instead they did nothing. That was the fourth ingredient for disaster.

A controversial report on the incident, written by Dr John Lawrence – controversial because he was asked to look into the incident and report on it although he is a member of the Board of South West Water – said: 'I have observed two reasons why this was not done. No manager took charge in the way implied [i.e. overall control] and there seems to be a culture in which the public are told as little as possible and expected to trust the Authority to look after their interests.' The word 'culture' is an interesting one for the same word was used to describe the general attitude permeating the upper management of London Transport and London Underground Ltd.

The water continued flowing through the mains supply.

On the day realization finally dawned, the head of community medicine in Cornwall, Dr Grainger, was informed of 'low pH levels in the water' and also of 'elevated aluminium levels'. Nothing more.

On 12 July he was contacted again and told of aluminium levels in the water as high as 4 mg. peaking to 40 mg. He believed the problem was over and also that the incident would not affect dialysis patients unless levels remained high for weeks. As Dr Lawrence says: 'Since he had received no complaints he took no positive action.'

Any queries from the general public were still met with the response that the water was safe to drink.

On 19 July a public meeting was called in Camelford, and Douglas Cross warned local people that they should not drink the water and that there were high aluminium levels in it.

Mr John Lewis, the district manager for South West Water who was later sacked by the authority, said in a sworn statement that he had realized as early as 7 a.m. on 7 July that there was possible contamination and by 8 July knew it was from aluminium sulphate. In his statement he said:

> The cause was confirmed on 12 July. On that day my head of operations, Mr Leslie Hicks phoned me from his office and told me it was confirmed that the load of aluminium sulphate had been discharged and that I must treat this information as strictly confidential and not tell anyone not already aware of the cause.

Finally on 20 July John Lewis was contacted by Geoffrey Smith, the regional operations engineer, who said he thought a press release should be issued giving the cause of the incident. John Lewis said this could only be done without the approval of the chairman and chief executive of SWWA, Keith Court. In fact a meeting was held to discuss such a measure but it was vetoed by Mr Court. Instead it was decided to put an advertisement in the press.

On 22 July – sixteen days after the accident – a single advertisement was placed in one issue of the *Western Morning News*. It appeared on the sports page. Headed 'South West Water – Water Supply Quality' and addressed to 'residents in the Camelford area', it began: 'South West Water wish to assure all their customers in North Cornwall that the water supply is fit to use and drink'. The aluminium as delivered to the works, it went on, 'was no more acidic than lemon juice and was further diluted many times'.

This remarkable statement was the *first* public admission that there had been an accident at all.

As Dr Neil Ward, an export on metal pollution from the University of Surrey was later to say, the advertisement was 'pathetic'. The assurance that the water was safe, made by South West Water, was totally unfounded and no evidence was provided to back the making of such a statement. The analogy with lemon juice was ridiculous. 'I mean, we don't flush lemon juice through our water system and then actually drink the water and lemon juice does not contain aluminium at the type of level which is associated with the introduction of aluminium sulphate into the water system'. Such a statement, he said, was 'very, very naive'.

The immediate effects on the population were, as we have seen, pretty terrible, especially for arthritic patients who spoke weeks later of the agonizing pains in their joints. A young man who had been involved in an accident and had a recent wound found it re-opened and bled for a month.

But it is the long-term implications which are the most worrying and these are still unclear. For a variety of reasons the district health authority did not take any immediate action and it was not until the autumn of 1988 that they finally circulated some 1,000 residents in the affected area with questionnaires as to their symptoms.

The long-term implications do not just apply to aluminium sulphate contamination but to the fact that the water which contained it, in its extremely caustic condition, caused leaching from water pipes and this has meant that copper, lead and even zinc also leached into the water supply and was taken into the systems of the unsuspecting people who drank it. In fact they drank a cocktail of metal-contaminated water.

The reason those with arthritis suffered so badly is that aluminium does not just leach metal out of pipes, it leaches calcium out of bones, which had a direct effect on the arthritic joints of the sufferers. There are obviously implications in the long term but not just for those with arthritis. Women are, as we know, especially vulnerable to osteoporosis, or bone loss, after the menopause when their oestrogen levels drop. Only time will tell if the incident will make this more likely.

The aluminium will cause numerous chemical reactions in the body and interact with those which actually control the welfare of our metabolic system, according to Dr Neil Ward. The eczemas, skin rashes and mouth ulcers which occurred after the pollution were, he said, direct results of the introduction of the aluminium.

There is also evidence that high levels of it can affect the behaviour patterns of children and dramatically affect the unborn child whose kidneys have not completely developed and cannot, therefore, excrete it. There are cases of babies dying as a result of high aluminium contamination while *in utero*. Kidneys in general are vulnerable to metal contamination.

Dr Ward and the local expert, Douglas Cross, disagree with the views of the local medical officers that there should be no long-term effects, feeling this is because they were not sufficiently informed or because they did not want to worry the local population unduly. According to Dr Ward, there should have been urine and blood tests carried out on individuals straight away. Questionnaires months after the event are insufficient.

Throughout this whole incident the local GP, Dr Richard Newman, proved to be a shining example of the best in NHS medicine. He realized straight away that there had been a major incident which caused the illnesses, had done his best to find out what had happened and, when he finally succeeded in this, he realized the implications of the incident without assistance from anyone. No doctor could have done more. He will now have to watch out for the long-term effects of the contamination, although it will be extremely difficult to prove that some condition which turns up years into the future is a direct result of the accident. For instance, there is now a growing belief among some experts that Alzheimer's disease, premature senile dementia, has a link with high levels of aluminium in the diet.

Calls for a full public inquiry and the resignation of the chairman and chief executive of South West Water, Keith Court, grew in strength in the weeks that followed the incident. Demands were also made by local MPs. Mr Court made it clear that he had no intention of resigning. Nor was there need for a public inquiry – Dr John Lawrence, a non-executive director on the Board of South West Water was to look into the incident and report.

As has already been noted this was not considered to be

satisfactory as he could not be said to be truly independent. In the event his report, published on 12 August 1988, was quite good so far as it went. It explained the series of events leading up to the contamination and its immediate results. It also heavily criticized SWWA.

Anyone could wander into the Lowermoor treatment works, isolated as it is on Bodmin Moor. A fence barred vehicles but there was pedestrian access. There was no labelling of external facilities to say what they were and there was nothing to show which was the aluminium sulphate storage tank. The aluminium sulphate system had been undergoing improvements and new tanks were not yet in use. The aluminium sulphate was pumped into the old tank. (Signs were later painted on to the tanks and buildings.)

Doors and manholes were mainly secured by padlocks and the key to the padlock on the gate also fitted many others including that on the aluminium sulphate tank – not an uncommon practice in the SWWA area. 'I find this totally unacceptable', said Dr Lawrence.

The regular driver held a key because it had been left hidden for him some time previously when he had made an unmonitored delivery. He had kept it until such time as he could return it but had not been back and so had not done so. He handed the key to the relief driver saying the tank was 'on the left'. So was the pure water tank. When the relief driver found the key fitted the pure water tank he thought he had found the right place. Dr Lawrence said the key should never have left the possession of SWWA.

The incident, continued Dr Lawrence, should never have occurred, but immediately its seriousness was recognized information should have passed up the line to the Head of Operations and an authoritative manager should have taken charge until the emergency was over. A plan of campaign should have been worked out to assess what the hazards were to consumers, industrial users and the environment, the precautions which should be taken and what SWWA had to do. There was no emergency plan.

All inquiries should have been met helpfully and the true position widely publicized. All the relevant medical authorities should have been fully informed.

Dr Lawrence's report made a string of recommendations with regard to the running of stations like Lowermoor to ensure that such an accident could not happen again. He also wanted better monitoring of the water in general. Alternative sources, the 'bowsers' which take water into the streets, were finally provided but often not well publicized and 'came and went without warning'. This should be improved.

He was concerned too over the function of the Community Medical Officer. The SWWA employs a medical consultant when needed but does not employ full-time staff. Information on possible hazards has to be done, he said, by medically qualified people and he suggested that the roles of the water authority and public health authorities be reviewed 'urgently' to remove ambiguity and ensure that they work effectively in the event of a more serious incident.

But, as has already been said, the report was only good so far as it went. Dr Lawrence, who admitted he was no specialist in the field of human reaction to internal metal contamination, said on the advice he has received that there should be no long-term effects. Others, as we have seen, do not agree. The admitted levels of aluminium in the water at one stage were 100 times the permitted limit but they might have been more. Water sent for analysis by independent experts since then has shown higher levels of contamination than SWWA say are present.

Perhaps, most crucially, he did not emphasize what becomes glaringly obvious from his report – that just about *anything* could have been tipped into that insecure pure water tank, from neat pesticide to arsenic.

The people of the area are very angry indeed. A lot of them were still ill months after the event and the water at the time of writing still contains significant amounts of copper, zinc and lead as well as aluminium. Women who drank the water in the early stages of pregnancy, or who have become pregnant since, are having to wait and see if it will affect their unborn children. All of them are fearful of possible long-term effects.

In spite of Dr Lawrence's report they want a proper public inquiry. They do not think a questionnaire about symptoms is what is needed; plenty of data is already available on symptoms. They want a full epidemiological survey to be carried out.

They want adequate compensation – and numerous writs are now in against SWWA. They, and many other people, want chairman Keith Court's head on a plate. They want his resignation.

In this story the unfortunate district manager played a comparable role to that of the assistant bosun on the *Herald of Free Enterprise*. The district manager was sacked on 13 September 1988 (his case has gone to appeal). Keith Court here played the role of Sir Jeffrey Sterling of P & O, and he also sees no reason whatsoever why he should resign.

Says Dr Neil Ward:

> I think, basically, one could look on this as a major ecological disaster the like of which has not been recorded in Britain before . . . my biggest fear is that this whole incident will just be put under the carpet as the old saying goes, will soon be forgotten because it is an isolated community, because the powers of responsibility are at a distance and therefore people will just forget what happened here. That is totally irresponsible to the citizens who live here.

Moreover, because of the way it was handled it provides no information that would help if a similar disaster should occur again.

This was a story which only seeped out. I am indebted almost entirely for the information used to Television South West and their researcher, Will Thorn. A programme on the subject was carried by TSW on the local network on 14 November 1988 under the title given to this chapter, 'A Trust Betrayed'.

For, make no mistake about it – a trust was betrayed; the trust of ordinary people that the water they drink is clean and uncontaminated and that if pollution should, accidentally, occur they would be informed immediately.

On 28 July 1988 – three weeks after the Lowermoor incident – South West Water announced a profit of £33.2m. This was the sixth year it had made a profit and was a rise of £4.9m over the previous year. This was the net profit – what was described by South West Water as a 'record total', £102.9m, was paid out by Mr Keith Court's consumers. The people of North Cornwall were offered a 10 per cent reduction in their current water bills.

Footnote

On 18 December 1988 water officials admitted that the amount of pollution suffered by the people of North Cornwall had been grossly underestimated. Analysis of water samples carried out by independent experts shortly after the incident found that the water had been contaminated by a staggering *6,000 times* the maximum levels considered safe by the EEC and the World Health Organization. Original figures had shown the water samples contained 620 mg per litre of aluminium – 3,100 times the EEC limit, but South West Water has now accepted that the real figure was approximately 1,200 mg. per litre.

The samples had been collected by Douglas Cross, who said he had made them available immediately after the accident, but had been ignored by local environment health officials.

The implications of what happened at Lowermoor are immense in view of imminent water privatization.

Postscript: Clapham Junction

Over the weekend of 28 August 1988 a passenger fell to his death from a crowded train travelling at 100 mph between Doncaster and York. All the seats were full, even the aisles crammed solid with holidaymakers, and he was leaning against an outside door when it flew open. An internal inquiry was held and the results are still not known but, according to *The Sunday Times* (28 August 1988), at the time a spokesman admitted to that newspaper that the door lock was not defective and that 'overcrowding was a possible "indirect" cause' of the accident.

In the morning of 12 December 1988 station staff at Euston dressed up like sardines – to the amusement of the reporters on Radio 4's, *Today* programme that morning – to draw attention to the situation on commuter trains from north of the capital and to plead for higher investment for the railways. Like everything else these days, the railways are expected to pay their way – something unheard of elsewhere in Europe where they are still considered to be a public service. Government subsidy to British Rail has been halved in the last five years. The 'sardines' were enlisting support for the Better Rail Campaign, a £550m self-financing programme over two years, designed by the independent National Economic Research Associates to increase services and reduce overcrowding.

At the time when passengers were somewhat ruefully smiling at the sardines, the driver of the 7.18 a.m. train from Basingstoke to Waterloo apparently discovered something wrong with the signals just outside Clapham Junction. He had no radio in his cab so he had to stop the train, climb out and telephone down the line to find out what was wrong.

Coming down the same line, immediately behind him, was

what should have been the 6.14 a.m. from Poole but vandals had pushed a concrete mixer on to the track the previous day and a train had collided with it. So passengers had had to join the train at Bournemouth. This train crashed into the one from Basingstoke; we do not know what the driver saw in the way of signals as he appears to have been killed outright. Within a couple of minutes an empty train coming out of Waterloo collided with the wreckage of the first two. The time was 8.13 a.m. A fourth train was only prevented from joining the pile-up by the fast action of the guard from the Bournemouth train, who flagged it down only yards away.

Thirty-three people were killed and nearly 200 injured, some of them seriously. With a commendable promptness rarely seen today, British Rail accepted full responsibility within twelve hours of the disaster which was, apparently, due to a signal failure. That afternoon Transport Minister Paul Channon was on his feet in the House of Commons for what is fast becoming something of a ritual following Zeebrugge and King's Cross – the Commons' statement that there has been a disaster, followed by the promise to set up a full public inquiry. That has been done but will obviously take months to report.

Signalling at Clapham Junction, one of the busiest stations in Europe, is currently undergoing a facelift – in fact work had been going on during the previous weekend along the actual length of track where the accident occurred. The present Clapham Junction signal box is a wooden shed hung over the railway lines operating a 1930s signalling system. The modernization has led to a string of 'temporary' signalling arrangements being put into operation. Trains pass through the junction at the rate of one every two minutes at peak hours and there had been complaints from drivers on a number of occasions about the temporary signalling systems.

Once again Mrs Thatcher was swiftly on the spot visiting victims in hospital – she noted she had done the same following Zeebrugge, King's Cross and Piper Alpha. Asked about overcrowding being a possible factor in the roll of death and injury, she said: 'When people want to get in, in the morning, they do tend to clamber on to the train even if it means standing, because they are anxious to get to their destination.'

The number of passengers travelling into London each day via Network South East has increased 15 per cent in the last three years. Nor is that the only region with difficulties. During November 1988 when old age pensioners were able to travel on cheap concessionary fares, trains to the west country were crammed with standing passengers, many of them very elderly. A British Rail spokesman told the writer at the time that they could not put on extra coaches as it was not economic.

In the summer of 1988 the Central Transport Consultative Committee, which represents railway passengers, published a report in which it said overcrowding had become an 'epidemic' that had to be cured. It said:

> In the case of Network South East, the CTCC remains profoundly unhappy about peak train loadings. The existing load factor standards, 110% for slammed door stock, 135% for sliding door trains, were intended as maximum loadings – not an average target to be aimed at. These maximum loadings are now exceeded regularly creating unacceptable levels of overcrowding on some routes, forcing people to stand far longer than the 20-minute maximum agreed between BR and the Government.

In November 1988 the Chief Inspector of Railways, recognizing growing public concern about the safety implications of overcrowding, said there was no evidence that it might cause accidents. This is probably true – the queries arise as to how many more people might be injured because they were standing rather than sitting at the time of an accident.

At the time of the train crash, 1500 people were crammed and standing in just twenty coaches on what is popularly known as 'the cattle-truck line'.

There is no legal limit on how many people can travel on any one train.

Within days of the crash – as is usual in these cases – various warnings came to light. On 14 December a number of newspapers carried a statement from a south London railway worker, Mr Stephen Jackson, who has worked at the East Putney signal box for eight years. He alleged that a similar fault to that which caused the Clapham disaster had occurred earlier in the year, but that the incident had been hushed up. He told BBC's

'Kilroy' programme on 13 December 1988 that, in March 1988, he had prevented a passenger train from hitting the back of a stationary train after a 'flickering signal' failed. He had had to run out and wave the oncoming driver down. He said he reported it but was told he must be wrong, and that the last thing that was wanted was a big inquiry. 'But', he told the BBC, 'in my mind I did not make a mistake'.

A spokesman for the National Union of Railwaymen (NUR) confirmed this to the writer, together with a number of other statements made during the 48 hours after the crash. British Rail staff complained that sometimes they could not even get into their own guard's van owing to the mass of people jammed into the train; and, most worryingly, that some guards who had refused to take out trains they considered dangerously overloaded, were told to get the trains out or face disciplinary action, including suspension.

NUR Secretary Jimmy Knapp said that the union had been warning British Rail for the last two years about the consequences of overcrowding, especially on Southern Region. 'Only last year the NUR surveyed guards all over Britain who reported persistent, chronic and dangerous overcrowding.' The NUR report told of a 360-seat commuter service from West Croydon to London Bridge which had travelled with 400 standing (yes, four hundred!) for more than twenty minutes, registering a load factor of 211 per cent – but even that was not as high as one between Ilkley and Leeds which registered 223 per cent.

The NUR spokesman told the writer that four years ago British Rail had embarked on what it described as a strict 'tight resourcing plan' with regard to both rolling stock and staffing, even if this meant that at peak times profitable passenger traffic literally had to be turned away. Profitability had to come first. He was particularly concerned to learn that at an internal meeting one of British Rail's senior engineers had said they were now 'looking for engineers prepared to take risks'.

Whether risks were taken or not remains to be proved at the full public inquiry, but more disturbing pointers emerged within a week of the crash. First, British Rail confirmed on 16 December that there had been a signal failure in November 1987, similar to that which occurred causing the Clapham crash. A driver travelling from Waterloo to Wimbledon stopped his late night train at a red signal outside the station. This then turned green but he realized, from his knowledge of the layout of the lines, that the points had not been switched over and he was actually moving the *wrong way* down a main line.

He stopped just outside the station and ran across the tracks to confirm with the signal box that operators had actually given him the green light. Recabling work had been going on at the time and it appears that 'bared older cables touched the terminals of other circuits'.

By the end of the week following the Clapham disaster the findings of British Rail's own internal inquiry had been widely leaked. It transpired that a British Rail team installing new signalling for Clapham Junction had been working twelve hours a day, seven days a week, for nearly six weeks and that in one case – according to the NUR – one man had been doing the work previously undertaken by six.

It is terrifying to contemplate but it seems that the night before the crash a short-staffed team, working under pressure, were actually trying to sort out the cabling for one of the busiest stretches of railway line in the world in cramped conditions, underneath the signalbox – using only *torchlight*!

The findings of the internal inquiry, which appeared in the media, were:

(1) that tired technicians had worked all night by torchlight and had left a single wire loose;
(2) this touched a nearby terminal on the fateful Monday morning, triggering off the faulty signal;
(3) an inspector had passed the faulty work as all right;
(4) there are unsatisfactory working practices in the signal department;
(5) drivers had passed the flickering signal but on seeing a clear line of green signals ahead, ignored it and carried on regardless.

Even while this inquiry was progressing, Scottish members of the NUR were turning down plans to extend their working day to thirteen hours for track maintenance crews; while plans are also well in hand drastically to reduce the number of signalling staff and to cut back further on maintenance.

At the time of writing we do not know how much the type of old rolling stock involved also contributed to the loss of life but Richard Hope, the editor of *The Railway Gazette*, told the media that British Rail was still using outdated Mark I coaches on Southern Region which were 'relatively weak' when compared with later Mark II and Mark III coaches. The construction of Mark I coaches makes them extremely vulnerable in the event of collision.

We shall have to await the findings of the public inquiry to know if safety was a casualty of the pressure on British Rail to pay its way and fatten itself up for privatization. Certainly the facts are ominous – the staffing cutbacks, the overworked team working by torchlight. We have heard it all before. At the time of the accident British Rail had set Network South East the task of reducing its grant requirement to £155m in 1989 and to £86m by 1992/93, compared to a subsidy of £350m paid to it in 1983.

In 1987 Mr Stanley Hall, a former chief signalling and safety officer with British Rail warned that without an entirely new signalling system train crashes would be inevitable, and he called for a strict train monitoring system. His warning came in a book published at a time when the latest report of the Rail Inspectorate had shown deaths and major injuries up by 62 per cent over five years, collisions up by 18 per cent and derailments by 6 per cent. The book was called *Bad Signals*.

Appendix

1   P&O European Ferries Dover   Internal Memorandum

To: Senior Master, All Vessels   From: Mr. M. Chaston
     Ship Management Team, All Vessels
     Ratings Noticeboards, All Vessels   Date: 8th July 1988

cc: Mr. M. Ridley
     Capt. Cairns
     Mr. I. F. G. Beard
     Mr. C. A. Howatt

Will you please ensure that the following information is conveyed to all Ratings as soon as practicable.

PENSION SCHEME OPTIONS

Investigations are continuing with the Merchant Navy Ratings Pension Fund (MNRPF) as to whether or not the rules of that scheme will allow Ratings to contribute who are not registered with the British Shipping Federation.

We understand that a decision will be reached before the end of July and once this is clarified we will advise.

As an alternative, the P&O Pension scheme is available to all employees of the Group, details are available from the Personnel Department.

Both schemes include a death-in-service benefit.

LEGAL EXPENSES COVER

We are advised by Brokers the following insurance cover can be available based on 1700 Ratings.

1   Legal expenses in pursuing death and/or personal injury at work claims,
2   Employment cover pursuing unfair dismissal, sex discrimination, etc.,
3   Defending criminal prosecutions, Health and Safety, leaving bow doors open, etc.,
4   Free legal advice.

The cost of this is approximately £3.40 per head per annum based on 100% membership.

The question of administration needs to be decided. One suggestion is that this can be carried out by the existing Ratings' Benevolent Fund Committee.

It would be appreciated if the Senior Ratings on the management team ascertain the collective view of their crews and, once known, advise myself via the Senior Master.

ANNUAL WAGE NEGOTIATIONS

Under these new arrangements there will be no direct negotiations on salaries – Ratings salaries will automatically increase in line with National Maritime Board percentage increase as they apply to the SGIA.

In addition to this, and unique to shipping, this Company has introduced two schemes to improve the remuneration package i.e.

Profit sharing scheme, which means, if the Company makes a profit in a year, a proportion will be paid to employees as a cash bonus.

P&O Group Profit Share Scheme After five years of service, employees are entitled to benefit from this scheme where, subject to the Group's profit, each eligible employee is allocated a number of shares in the Company, and like all shareholders, receive cash dividends from those shares.

MEDICAL CARE

Any Rating who is in need of medical care via the Dreadnought wing at St. Thomas Hospital, London, can make arrangements either direct by the individual's own Doctor, or through the Welfare Section of the Personnel Department Dover (0304) 223279.

[Signed]
M. CHASTON
Personnel Manager

2 Letter from Nicholas Ridley, Secretary of State for Transport, to London Regional Transport, 20 JULY 1984

Mr. Forman asked the Secretary of State for Transport when he proposes to announce the Government's objectives for London Regional Transport.

   Mr. Nicholas Ridley: I have today written to the chairman of London Regional Transport in the following terms:

"1   This letter concerns the objectives which the Government wishes you to pursue in running London Regional Transport. It supplements the statutory and financial duties of the Board. Enactment of the London Regional Transport Act starts a new stage in providing better and more efficient public transport for the capital city. The Act sets the framework of duties for you and your colleagues, and prescribes how you are to publish your plans and strategies and consult on them with local authorities and others. Close working with British Rail is specially important, and I am writing separately to you and to the Chairman of the British Railways Board about that.

Tasks for London Regional Transport
2   Building upon the White Paper "Transport in London", I see four initial tasks for the new organisation:

— provide bus and underground services for London within the resources available and to make the service more attractive to the public;
— to reduce costs, including fraud, and the call on taxpayers' and ratepayers' money and generally secure better value for the community;
— to involve the private sector in the provision of services where that is more efficient and to make better use of publicly owned assets, including the sale of public assets which are no longer required;
— to promote better management through smaller and more efficient units with clear goals and measurable objectives.

Cost, Subsidy, Fares and Investment
3   I want you to submit for my approval within an investment allocation that will be agreed by the Government, a programme of investment to modernise the public transport systems, making them more attractive to passengers and more efficient. In addition to necessary renewal of equipment, you will want to bring forward as

rapidly as possible investments which will save costs, and a steady programme to improve facilities for passengers, including interchanges between bus, rail and underground services, long distance coaches, taxis and private transport. I shall expect you to secure this investment at the best price through competition wherever possible.

4   To reduce the present excessive call on ratepayers and taxpayers, the burden of revenue support will have to be reduced. To achieve this, a proper priority for investment is vital. You have told me that you can achieve a reduction in unit costs of two and a half per cent. a year, in real terms, over the next few years. I look to you, if possible, to do better than that, and I shall want to review the target with you within the next twelve months. The most effective use of labour, and keen purchasing in the market, will both be important in achieving this target.

5   The improvement of efficiency can make a large contribution to achieving your prime financial target, which will be to reduce the level of revenue support from ratepayers and taxpayers to £95m in cash in 1987–88. Given control of costs, this does not in any way imply a programme of large fare rises. After any initial increase to redress the balance I would expect you to maintain a broadly stable relationship between fares, prices generally and the fares on the British Rail London commuter services. You will also want to consider how your fare scales can best be set to reflect the different cost structure of the bus and underground systems.

6   In the light of these objectives and your plans to achieve them the Government will decide each autumn the provision for your total of external finance for the coming fiscal year; and your investment allocation.

Organisation and Control

7   I look forward to receiving by the end of the year your proposals under the Act for establishing separate bus and underground subsidiaries, and separate companies for other parts of your organisation. These should provide for the clear identification of costs and performance and clear responsibility for them, and for the involvement of private capital where appropriate.

8   In the case of the bus subsidiary, the organisation will need to allow your Board to set clear objectives for devolving accountable management to smaller units, for reducing costs per bus mile, for improving the match between supply and demand so as to increase average bus loadings, and for carrying forward vigorously a plan to bring in other operators, both public and private, to compete for the provision of services.

Disabled People

9   The Act requires you to have regard to the needs of disabled people and to report annually on the steps you have taken to cater for them. I expect you to keep their requirements in mind in developing your equipment, and co-operate with those financing special services for the more severely disabled. I hope that one member of your Board can provide a focal point for considering the needs of disabled people.

Conclusion

10   In seeking to improve bus and underground services for London you will be strengthened by advice from the new London Regional Passengers' Committee.

11   Your efforts to provide better value for money in public transport will have the fullest support of the Government and I am sure of the ratepayers and of the travelling public."

3 Inspection by London Fire Brigade 1988

KING'S CROSS   (NORTHERN LINE – 24 MARCH 1988)

1 Rubbish to be removed from working area at top of Northern Line escalators.
2 Permanent way mess room – hurricane lamps to be removed.
3 Permanent way utility room platform 5 needs tidying up and should be kept locked.
4 Plans should be stored away from electrical cupboards in AET room Northern Line.
5 Room E17 replace door.
6 Platform 7 permanent way utility room – unable to gain access.
7 Victoria Line southbound – decorative panel to be replaced.
8 Victoria Line south permanent way utility room – lids to be put on grease tins and rags to be stored away.

TOTTENHAM COURT ROAD
(NORTHERN LINE – 24 MARCH 1988)

1 The sign 'FIRE HYDRANT' should be replaced by a sign to the effect 'HOSE REEL' on the cabinet door.
2 The fire doors of the ticket office should not be propped open and the fire extinguishers should not be moved from their fittings.
3 The defective bin in the permanent way store room should be replaced.
4 The hydrant wheel is too close to the panel and therefore the panel should be moved slightly.
5 The paper sack and rubbish found in the staff toilet should be removed.
6 The electrical cables in the subway behind SMS office should be tidied up and the old redundant cables removed.
7 The buckets, mop and mobile scaffolding found in the CER (switchroom) should be removed.
8 The chair, bench and ladder found in the CER (above ops room) should be removed.
9 The fluff and grease on escalator 6 should be removed.
10 The means of escape hatch from the lower escalator room on the Northern Line is not easily openable.
11 The hand winding gear for escalator 1 should be hung on a bracket and labelled accordingly.

12 Guards should be provided for the spindles of nos. 1 and 2 escalator motors.
13 One new oil storage bin should be provided.
14 The disused water fire extinguisher and roll of electrical cable should be removed.
15 The transformer is at present obstructing the emergency exit between the top and lower machine rooms and should be removed.
16 LFB Fog Inlet

    (a) adequate wording indicating the area to be covered should be provided

    (b) the electrical switches in the inlet boxes should be resited.

EUSTON   (NORTHERN LINE – 2/3 MARCH 1988)

1 The paper used to block the ceiling ventilation louvres in the ticket office should be removed.
2 The combustible materials (papers) stored on the floor of the Chief Clerk's store room should be removed and stored in a locker.
3 The fire extinguishers provided by the contractors for the working site in the disused lift shafts should be renewed as they are out of date.
4 Upper level – communications room – rubbish should be removed.
5 Victoria Line northbound – rubbish should be removed from the cleaning services and permanent way stores.
6 Platform 1 – old boxes and a chair should be removed from C.E.R.
7 Rubbish in the cleaning services room stored in metal bins and the broken chair removed.
8 The fire exit door from the ticket office was not available for use as it was obstructed by storage and would not open. All self closing doors in the ticket office and P.O.M. room should be kept closed.
9 Escalator 3 & 4 – the hose reel in the upper chamber was not working. A large accumulation of dust was found on all electrical installations.
10 Switchroom E4 – the wooden boxes stored in the space above the ceiling should be removed.
11 The rubbish in the disused running tunnel should be removed.

WARREN STREET   (NORTHERN LINE – 2/3 MARCH 1988)

1 The bin room and the room in escalators 4 & 6 machine room were not inspected as no key was available.

2 Charing Cross line southbound – the rubbish in the trap of the anti-suicide pit should be removed.
3 Victoria Line escalator room 3 & 4 – the Carbon Dioxide fire extinguisher should be rehung on the wall.
4 A large build-up of dust existed by escalator 9.
5 The Carbon Dioxide fire extinguisher in the booking offices kitchen was apparently empty and required replacement.

GOODGE STREET   (NORTHERN LINE – 2/3 MARCH 1988)

1 The electric heater in the contractors site office by the ticket halls entrance should not be left unattended.
2 The defective light switch in the relay room should be replaced.
3 The locks to the hydrant cupboards require repairing.

MORNINGTON CRESCENT
(NORTHERN LINE – 2/3 MARCH 1988)

1 The timber slats and rubbish at the bottom of the stairs in the disused subway should be removed.
2 The rubbish in the main tunnel fan corridor should be removed.
3 Southbound platform

   (a) FIRE RESISTING glazing is required in the permanent way store doors. These doors should also be set in the wall correctly.
   (b) the high level vent holes should be filled in if health and safety requirements permit.
   (c) the FIRE RESISTING glazing in the doors of the through permanent way store should be fixed properly. The area over these doors should be made half hour FIRE RESISTING.

4 The station plan box sited behind the ticket office is impossible to reach.
5 A quantity of rubbish which is situated around the door of the mess room should be removed.
6 The rubbish situated around the access door to the lift motor room should be removed. A new storage bin for oil should be provided in this room.
7 The water fire extinguisher requires servicing.

Bibliography

1 Disasters

Destination Disaster, by Paul Eddy, Elaine Potter and Bruce Page (Times Newspapers, 1976).
Which?, September 1988.

2 Zeebrugge

Report of Formal Investigation into the loss of the Herald of Free Enterprise (HMSO, 1988).
Minutes of Procedures of the Formal Investigation.
The Safety and Vulnerability of Ro-Ro ships (Royal Institution of Naval Architects, March 1988).
Journal of the Nautical Institute, May 1988.
Affidavit of John Douglas Ball, 21 July 1988.
Disaster at Zeebrugge – the Crew's Story (National Union of Seamen, 1987).
Hansard, 11 May 1988.

3 King's Cross

Submissions of the Fire Brigades Union to the Committee of Investigation into the King's Cross Fire.
Evidence to the Inquiry into the Events at King's Cross Underground Station Disaster 18 November 1987 (Fire Brigades Union).
Submission by the Associated Society of Locomotive Engineers and Firemen to the Committee of Investigation into the King's Cross Underground Fire.
Report of the Annual Fire Inspection – Deep Tube Lines and Stations, 30 November 1987.
Learning Lessons – The King's Cross Aftermath (London Fire and Civil Defence Authority).

4 Piper Alpha

This chapter was based on interviews, press cuttings and information supplied by the MSF and oil workers.

5 Air Traffic Control and Pilot Fatigue

Flight Fatigue, Report of the Special Committee of the British Air Line Pilots' Association, February 1973. (This was published and then immediately suppressed.)

Evidence to the House of Commons Transport Committee Inquiry into Air Traffic Control Safety, Volumes 1 and 2; and Supplementary Statement (Institution of Professional Civil Servants, June 1988).

CHIRP reports, 'Confidential Human Factors Incident Reporting Programme', in *Feedback.*

6 At Sea – Dropping the Pilot and Ro-Ro Ferries

The Safety and Vulnerability of Ro-Ro ships (Royal Institution of Naval Architects, March 1988).

Journal of the Nautical Institute, May 1988.

Information provided by ex-Trinity House pilots.

7 The Channel Tunnel

Parked Car Fires, paper by John A. Butler C.Eng., M.I.Mech., EMI Fire, College of Technology, Dublin (January 1987).

Fire Hazard in the Channel Tunnel, by H. S. Eisner (*Tunnels and Tunnelling,* September 1988).

Transportation of People, by R. B. Blackburn, OBE, QFSM, F.I. Fire C. (January 1987).

The Channel Tunnel, by Sir Kenneth Holland, CBE (January 1987).

8 Going Critical – Nuclear Power

Red Alert, by Judith Cook (NEL, 1986).

Britain's Nuclear Nightmare, by J. Cutler and R. Edwards (Sphere Books: London, 1988).

Three Mile Island – Thirty Minutes to Meltdown, by Daniel Ford (Viking: New York, 1982).

The Worst Accident in the World, by staff of the *Observer* (Pan Books: London, 1986).

The Gravedigger's Dilemma, by Renee Chudleigh and William Cannell (Friends of the Earth 1984).

Health Service Arrangements for Dealing with Nuclear Accidents, DHSS Circular HC (85) 24, Supplement to HC (77)1.

Risks of Nuclear Power Reactors: A Review of NRC Safety Study WASH-1400 (Cambridge, Mass., Union of Concerned Scientists, 1977).

Accidents Will Happen, by Francis Nectoux and William Cannell (Earth Resources Research/Friends of the Earth, 1984).

Nuclear Regulatory Commission Policy Statement on the Reactor Safety Study and Review by the Lewis Panel (Washington, 1979).

Hinkley Point Power Station Public Inquiry – Statement of Case (Central Electricity Generating Board, 1988).

Submission of Evidence, by the Consortium of Opposing Local Authorities to Hinkley Point Power Station Public Inquiry, 1988.

9 Pollution – the Slow Burning Fuse

The Price of Freedom, by Judith Cook (NEL, 1985/6).

The Hole in the Sky, by John Gribbin (Corgi, 1987).

Food Adulteration and How to Beat it, London Food Commission (Unwin Hyman, 1988).

The Scientific Management of Hazardous Waste, by Fuller and Willets (Cambridge University Press, 1983).

Hazardous Waste in America, by S. S. Epstein *et al.* (San Francisco, 1982).

Nuclear Disaster in the Urals, by Zhores A. Medveder (Angus & Robertson: London, 1979).

Nuclear Power and the Environment, Flowers Report, Royal Commission on Environmental Pollution (HMSO, 1976).

Agriculture and Pollution, Kornberg Report, Royal Commission on Environmental Pollution (HMSO, 1979).

First Report on Radioactive Waste 1985–1986, House of Commons Select Committee on the Environment, (HMSO).

Disposal of Radioactive Waste (briefing paper) (Cambridge, Mass., 1984).

Hazardous Waste Dump at Koko, Bendel State, Nigeria, Report, Aspinwall & Co. Ltd. 1988.

Risk of an Environmental Disaster (Friends of the Earth, 1988).

Pesticide Residues in Food (London Food Commission, 1986).

Epilogue

Report of an Inquiry into an incident at Lowermoor Water Treatment Works of the South West Water Authority on 6 July 1988, by Dr. John Lawrence.

Index